Nuclei
and Radioactivity

Gregory R. Choppin
Florida State University

1964

W. A. BENJAMIN, INC. New York Amsterdam

NUCLEI AND RADIOACTIVITY

Final manuscript was put into production on March 27,
    1963; this volume was published May 15, 1964.

The publisher is pleased to acknowledge the assistance
    of Lenore Stevens, who copyedited the manuscript,
    and William Prokos, who produced the illustrations.

W. A. BENJAMIN, INC.,
2465 Broadway, New York 10025

Editor's Foreword

THE TEACHING OF GENERAL CHEMISTRY to beginning students becomes each day a more challenging and rewarding task as subject matter becomes more diverse and more complex and as the high school preparation of the student improves. These challenges have evoked a number of responses; this series of monographs for general chemistry is one such response. It is an experiment in the teaching of chemistry which recognizes a number of the problems that plague those who select textbooks and teach chemistry. First, it recognizes that no single book can physically encompass all the various aspects of chemistry that all instructors collectively deem important. Second, it recognizes that no single author is capable of writing authoritatively on *all* the topics that are included in everybody's list of what constitutes general chemistry. Finally, it recognizes the instructor's right to choose those topics that he considers to be important without having to apologize for having omitted large parts of an extensive textbook.

This volume, then, is one of approximately fifteen in the General Chemistry Monograph Series, each written by one or more highly qualified persons very familiar with the current status of the subject by virtue of research in it and also conversant with the problems associated with teaching the subject matter to beginning students. Each volume deals broadly with one of the subdivisions of general chemistry and constitutes a complete entity, far more comprehensive in its coverage than is permitted by the limitation of the standard one-volume text. Taken together, these volumes provide a range of topics from which the individual instructor can easily select those that will provide for his class an appropriate coverage of the material he considers most important.

Furthermore, inclusion of a number of topics that have only recently been considered for general chemistry courses, such as thermodynamics, molecular spectroscopy, and biochemistry, is planned, and these volumes will soon be available. In every instance a modern structural point of view has been adopted with the emphasis on general principles and unifying theory.

These volumes will have other uses also: selected monographs can be used to enrich the more conventional course of study by providing readily available, inexpensive supplements to standard texts. They should also prove valuable to students in other areas of the physical and biological sciences needing supplementary information in any field of chemistry pertinent to their own special interests. Thus, students of biology will find the monographs on biochemistry, organic chemistry, and reaction kinetics particularly useful. Beginning students in physics and meteorology will find the monograph on thermodynamics rewarding. Teachers of elementary science will also find these volumes invaluable aids to bringing them up to date in the various branches of chemistry.

Each monograph has several features which make it especially useful as an aid to teaching. These include a large number of solved examples and problems for the student, a glossary of technical terms, and copious illustrations.

The authors of the several monographs deserve much credit for their enthusiasm which made this experiment possible. Professor Rolfe Herber of Rutgers University has been of invaluable assistance in the preparation of this series, having supplied editorial comment and numerous valuable suggestions on each volume. Thanks are also due to Professor M. Kasha of the Florida State University for many suggestions during the planning stages and for reading several of the manuscripts.

RUSSELL JOHNSEN

Tallahassee, Florida
October 1962

Preface

The dramatic events that ended World War II thrust nuclear science into public consciousness. The prolonged world-wide debate on the testing of nuclear weapons, the rapid pace of both military and scientific developments in nuclear science and technology, the advances in such fields as medicine and agriculture through the use of radioisotopes have all maintained and increased this public interest. It is a common experience of teachers of first-year chemistry courses in universities that their students show this interest by their response to the lectures on nuclear chemistry. However, the brief chapter in the general chemistry textbooks can only mention some aspects of this field. Almost without exception the treatment is too sketchy, and such important areas as nuclear spectroscopy and nuclear reactions are virtually ignored.

In this book I have attempted to describe the important principles in nuclear science, as well as its major experimental tools. Emphasis, however, is on those areas of experimental and theoretical research of most concern to nuclear chemists today. Since this book is intended as a supplement to a first-year general chemistry course in college, the approach is qualitative. Also, in order to keep the length within reasonable limits, I have had to omit some topics and abbreviate my treatment of certain others. If I have achieved my goal and the reader finds that nuclear chemistry holds promise of exciting challenge, he is urged to continue his study with the texts listed in the bibliography.

GREGORY R. CHOPPIN

Tallahassee, Florida
October, 1963

Contents

Constants

Velocity of light	$c = 2.99776 \times 10^{10}$ cm/sec
Faraday constant	$F = 96500$ abs coul/g-equiv
Electronic charge	$e = 4.8025 \times 10^{-10}$ abs esu
	$= 1.60203 \times 10^{-19}$ abs coulombs
Planck constant	$h = 6.624 \times 10^{-27}$ erg-sec
Avogadro's number	$N = 6.0228 \times 10^{23}$ mole^{-1}
Mass of electron	$m = 9.1066 \times 10^{-28}$ g
Atomic weight of electron	$m = 5.4862 \times 10^{-4}$ (physical scale)
Mass of unit atomic weight	$M_o = 1.66035 \times 10^{-24}$ g
Nuclear radius	$R = 1.4 \times 10^{-13} A^{1/3}$ (A = mass number)

Atomic weights

hydrogen	$M_H = 1.00814$
helium	$M_{He} = 4.00387$
neutron	$M_n = 1.00899$
Energy equivalence	1 atomic mass unit = 931 MeV
	$= 1.49 \times 10^{-3}$ erg
	$= 3.56 \times 10^{-11}$ cal

1 electron mass = 0.510 MeV

$$1 \text{ MeV} = 1.07 \times 10^{-3} \text{ amu}$$
$$= 1.60 \times 10^{-6} \text{ erg}$$
$$= 3.82 \times 10^{-14} \text{ cal}$$

1 eV/molecule = 23.06 kcal/mole

I

The Nucleus

EVERYONE WHO READS NEWSPAPERS today is quite aware of the
atomic nucleus and the tremendous potential it has for mankind. It is not incorrect to say that the future of our civilization
is inextricably bound to the atomic nucleus. Either we shall use its
energy to abolish want on earth and to reach the planets or we will
use it to destroy ourselves. And yet, half a century ago the existence of the nucleus was unknown. By 1911 the phenomenon of

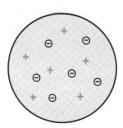
Thomson model

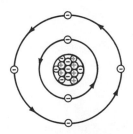
Rutherford model

**Figure 1-1 Representations of the models of the atom
suggested by J. J. Thomson ("grapes-in-jello" model) and
by E. Rutherford ("miniature-solar-system" model).**

radioactivity had been recognized for fifteen years, and much important research had been conducted with radioactive substances by the Curies and other scientists during the interval. Physicists and chemists accepted, albeit with reservations, the model of the atom proposed by J. J. Thomson in 1908 in which negatively charged particles—electrons—were dispersed in some orderly, fixed fashion in a continuous sphere of positive electricity, much like grapes in a bowl of jello (Fig. 1–1). Perhaps it will help to illustrate how recently this was to point out that if your grandfathers studied college physics, they were very probably taught this atomic model. Man knew how to fly, to use electricity, and to build automobiles well before he knew what an atom was really like.

DISCOVERY OF THE NUCLEUS

1–1 Alpha-Particle-Scattering Experiment

One of the leaders in the new physics of radioactivity was Ernest Rutherford (1871–1937), a physicist born in New Zealand who worked both in England and in Canada and who was raised to the peerage for his contributions to science. It had been observed by Rutherford and co-workers that when a stream of alpha particles emanating from a naturally radioactive substance such as a uranium or thorium salt was allowed to strike á photographic plate after traversing a thin sheet of metal, the beam edges were diffuse rather than sharp. This indicated that some of the alpha particles were being deflected and scattered in their passage through the metal. Especially interesting was the observation that, whereas the majority of beam particles passed through the metal foil undeflected or slightly deflected, a few particles suffered very large deflections—1 in every 8000 was deflected by more than 90° (Fig. 1–2). The nature of alpha particles was well known from earlier research by Rutherford; they possessed a double positive charge and a mass of 4 relative to hydrogen. For such heavy, charged particles to be deflected by the constituents of the Thomson model of the atom was unbelievable. In Rutherford's own words, "It was about as credible as if you had fired a 15-inch shell at a piece of tissue paper and it came back and hit you." There

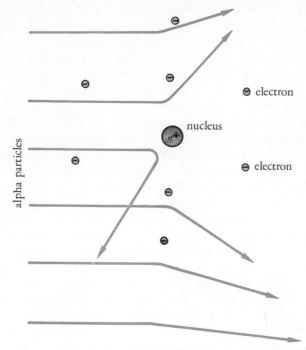

Figure 1–2   Scattering of alpha particles upon approach to an atomic nucleus.

were no electrostatic fields in the Thomson description of the atom great enough to cause such deflections either by attraction (negative fields) or by repulsion (positive fields).

1–2   Rutherford's Interpretation

In 1911 Lord Rutherford published a paper that offered an interpretation of his alpha-particle-scattering experiment and by so doing simultaneously gave birth to nuclear physics and provided the cornerstone of modern atomic physics. It was easy to calculate that the light, negative electrons of the atoms were incapable of causing large deflections of the heavy, positive alpha

particles by coulombic attraction such as exists between two elec-
trically dissimilar particles (e.g., between Na^+ and Cl^- ions in a
NaCl crystal). Therefore Rutherford postulated that the deflections were due to coulombic repulsion between the positive
alpha particles and another positively charged entity present in the
atom. The charge of this positive entity had to be sufficiently large
to produce the high-angle deflections. Also, since the vast majority of alpha particles passed through the metal relatively undeflected, this positively charged entity had to occupy a very small
portion of the total volume. The picture that emerged from such
reasoning was that the metal was composed of atoms, each having
a very small, heavy center called the nucleus where all the positive
charge and almost all the mass was concentrated. This positive
nucleus had, associated with it, a number of electrons sufficient to
produce electric neutrality in the atom as a whole. These electrons
were presumed to revolve around the nucleus in a fashion similar
to that of the planets about the sun, and their orbits filled the
volume of the atom. Two years later Niels Bohr (1886–1962), a
Danish physicist, proposed an atomic model that provided the
basis for understanding the behavior of the electrons in their
atomic orbits. Our main concern in this monograph, however, is
with the nucleus rather than with the extranuclear electrons that,
by their involvement in chemical bonds, determine the chemistry
of the elements.

CONSTITUENTS OF THE NUCLEUS

For several years after the initial description of the nucleus,
it was believed that the constituent particles were electrons and
protons. For the nitrogen atom of atomic number 7 and mass
number 14, the nucleus was thought to consist of 14 protons, each
having unit mass, and of 7 electrons, with a resultant net nuclear
charge of +7 that was balanced by the 7 extranuclear electrons.
Doubts concerning this nuclear model were expressed as early as
1920 by Rutherford and others. In 1932 James Chadwick demonstrated the existence of neutrons and provided the basis for a much
more satisfactory model, with the nucleus composed of only pro-

tons and neutrons. According to this model—the one that we use today—the nitrogen atom has a nucleus consisting of 7 protons and 7 neutrons. Since neutrons have no charge but are very similar to protons in mass, the net nuclear charge is $+7$ and the total mass number 14. There are still 7 extranuclear electrons. The mass number A is equal to the atomic number Z plus the neutron number N. Since Z equals the number of protons and N equals the number of neutrons, $A = Z + N = $ total number of nucleons (i.e., the total number of particles in the nucleus). The elemental identity is provided by the atomic number; e.g., any atom that has 19 (and *only* 19) protons is by definition potassium. However, of the atoms found in nature that have 19 protons in their nuclei, some have 20 neutrons ($A = 39$) whereas others have 22 neutrons ($A = 41$). Because the atomic number is constant even though the mass numbers are not, these are all atoms of potassium with the same chemical properties. Such atoms, of constant Z but different A, are isotopes of the same element.

NUCLEAR PROPERTIES

In the remainder of this chapter we shall discuss the principal properties of the nucleus—the mass, the energy, the size, the coulomb field, and the forces that hold it together.

1–3   Nuclear Mass

When two elements combine in a chemical system, the amount of heat evolved is a measure of the stability of the compound formed. The greater this heat of formation, the greater the stability of the compound. When carbon is combined with oxygen to form CO_2, it is found experimentally that 94.03 kcal of heat is evolved per mole of CO_2 formed. This is written

$$C + O_2 \rightarrow CO_2 + 94.03 \text{ kcal}$$

If the relationship of Einstein, $E = mc^2$, is used, it is possible to calculate the loss in mass in the system $C + O_2$ necessary to produce the 94.03 kcal of energy. According to the Einstein relation,

1 kcal $\approx$ 4.7 $\times$ 10^{-11} g; thus the total mass loss would be 4.4 $\times$ 10^{-9} g. Although scientists do not doubt that this mass loss actually occurs in the system, at present there are no instruments of sufficient sensitivity to measure such a very small change.

The energy changes in nuclear reactions are much larger than those in chemical reactions. For example, if a mole of the isotope of helium of mass number 4 (i.e., He^4) were to be formed by addition of a mole of neutrons to a mole of the isotope of helium of mass number 3 (i.e., He^3), 4.7 $\times$ 10^8 kcal of energy would be released. This would correspond to a decrease of 0.022 g, a change easily observable with our present instruments. As a matter of fact, it is not common practice to use mole quantities in considering nuclear reactions, as the number of individual reactions under all laboratory conditions is well below 6.02 $\times$ 10^{23}. Instead, the energy and mass changes involved in an individual reaction are the values used. The units utilized in thermochemistry are too large to be useful in this system, so new units have been chosen. For masses, the unit is the atomic mass unit (symbol: **amu**), by definition 1/16 the mass of the O^{16} atom and equal to 1.66 $\times$ 10^{-24} g. The neutron has a mass of 1.00893 amu, whereas the mass of the hydrogen atom is 1.00812 amu. For energies, the unit is the electron volt (symbol: **eV**), the energy acquired by a unit electronic charge when it is accelerated through a potential-difference of 1 volt. One eV is equal to 3.8 $\times$ 10^{-20} cal. Perhaps a more meaningful relationship between electron volts and calories is expressed

$$1 \text{ eV/molecule} = 23.06 \text{ kcal/mole} \qquad \textbf{\textit{(1–1)}}$$

The units keV (10^3 eV) and MeV (10^6 eV) are encountered very often in nuclear science.

Now let us reconsider our helium reaction. Nuclear reaction equations are written much like chemical equations, and it is necessary that both the total Z and the total A values be balanced on the two sides of the equation. The helium reaction is written

$$_2\text{He}^3 + {_0}n^1 \rightarrow {_2}\text{He}^4 + Q$$

The value of Q is 20.5 MeV. Since 1 amu = 931 MeV, the change in mass should be 20.5/931 amu or 0.022 amu. The numerical coincidence of 0.022 amu per reaction is merely a fortuitous combination of constants arising from the fact that a nucleon has a mass of approximately 1.000 amu. Using tabulated mass values,

$$M_{He^3} = 3.0170 \qquad M_{He^4} = 4.0039$$
$$\underline{M_n = 1.0089}$$
$$\text{total} = 4.0259$$

Therefore

$$\Delta M = (M_{He^3} + M_n) - (M_{He^4}) = (4.0259) - (4.0039)$$
$$= 0.0220 \text{ amu}$$

This result agrees perfectly with the value of Q as it must, of course, in accord with the **law of conservation of mass and energy.**

The same type of consideration applies to spontaneous disintegrations, such as the decay of U^{238} by alpha-particle emission.

$$_{92}U^{238} \rightarrow {}_{90}Th^{234} + {}_2He^4 + Q$$

$$\Delta M = (M_{U^{238}}) - (M_{Th^{234}} + M_{He^4}) = (238.1249)$$
$$- (234.1165 + 4.0039) = 0.0045 \text{ amu}$$

This loss of mass appears as the kinetic energy of alpha decay.

$$Q_\alpha = 931\Delta M = 931 \times 0.0045 = 4.2 \text{ MeV}$$

The masses used are those of the atoms rather than those of the nuclei. Atomic masses are relatively easy to measure experimentally whereas it is much more difficult to determine nuclear masses by direct experimental means. Provided that balance is kept in the number of electrons on both sides of the equation, the use of atomic rather than nuclear masses introduces no significant error. Notice that for the alpha-decay reaction of U^{238} there are 92 electrons associated with U^{238} on the left side and $90 + 2$ associated with Th^{234} and He^4 on the right side. There are a number of compilations of atomic masses, some experimental and some calculated. The compilation by Segré in Volume 1 of *Experimental Nuclear Physics* (Wiley, N.Y., 1953) is a good example of a useful source of such data.

1–4   Nuclear Binding Energy

Consider another system: the hypothetical formation of He⁴ from two neutrons and two hydrogen atoms.

$$2\,_1\mathrm{H}^1 + 2\,_0n^1 \rightarrow {}_2\mathrm{He}^4$$

The decrease in mass is

$$\Delta M = 2M_n + 2M_\mathrm{H} - M_\mathrm{He} = (2 \times 1.0090) + (2 \times 1.0081)$$
$$- (4.0039) = 0.0303 \text{ amu}$$

This means that 931 times 0.0303 or 28.1 MeV is liberated in the process. Although it is very unlikely that two neutrons and two protons would ever collide simultaneously to form He⁴, this calculation is useful because it indicates that to break He⁴ into its basic component nucleons would require at least 28.1 MeV. This is a significant amount of energy and shows He⁴ to be a particularly stable nucleus. A similar calculation for the isotope of hydrogen of $A = 2$—deuterium—gives a result of only 2.22 MeV, indicating that H² is relatively easy to dissociate into a neutron and a proton.

The energy necessary to decompose a nucleus into its individual component nucleons is known as the **binding energy** and has the same significance in nuclear science as the heat of formation has in chemical thermodynamics. If the binding energy is divided by the total number of nucleons A, the binding energy per nucleon (BE/A) is obtained and serves as a convenient measure of the stability of the nucleus. For He⁴ the value of BE/A is 28.1/4 or 7.0 MeV, whereas for H² it is 2.22/2 or 1.11 MeV. In Fig. 1–3, the values of BE/A for the stable nuclides are plotted as a function of their mass numbers.

One may observe from Fig. 1–3 that the curve is ascendant until $A \approx 60$. Therefore in this region, when two lighter nuclei are combined to form a heavier nucleus, the BE/A value of the heavier one is larger than those of the two lighter nuclei, signifying the release of energy. This combination (fusion) of light nuclei as a source of energy release is the principle upon which the hydrogen bomb is based. On the other hand, the curve in Fig. 1–3 descends as A increases beyond 60. In this region, fusion of lighter nuclei into a heavy one is not exothermic (energy-releas-

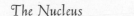
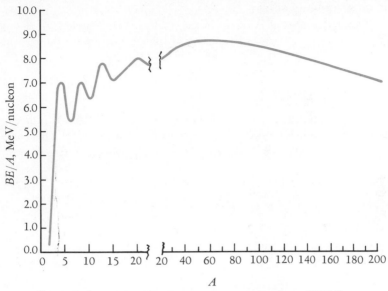

Figure 1–3 Plot of binding energy per nucleon (*BE/A*) as a function of mass number *A*.

ing) but rather endothermic (energy-absorbing). Conversely, dissociation (fission) of a heavy nucleus into two lighter nuclei goes from low *BE/A* values to higher ones and energy is liberated. This fission process is the source of the energy in atomic bombs and nuclear reactors.

Another feature of Fig. 1–3 is that, for $A > 3$, the values of *BE/A* do not vary greatly over the whole range of *A*, all lying between 5 and 8 MeV. To a first approximation, therefore, *BE/A* is almost constant. Since

$$BE/A \sim \text{constant}$$

then

$$BE \sim \text{constant} \times A$$

or

$$BE \propto A \qquad\qquad (1-2)$$

In other words, the total nuclear binding energy is roughly proportional to the total number of nucleons in the nucleus. The importance of this observation with respect to the nature of the force that holds the nucleus together is discussed more extensively in Sec. 1–7.

1–5   Nuclear Radius

Experimental measurements of the sizes of nuclei indicate that the volumes of nuclei are directly proportional to the total numbers of nucleons present, i.e., $V \propto A$. Since, for a sphere,

$$V \propto R^3$$

where R is the radius of the sphere, then

$$R^3 \propto A$$

or

$$R \propto A^{1/3} \qquad\qquad (1\text{–}3a)$$

Using R_0 as the proportionality constant,

$$R = R_0 A^{1/3} \qquad\qquad (1\text{–}3b)$$

Rutherford proved by his scattering experiments that the nucleus occupies a very small portion of the total volume of the atom. Roughly, the radii of nuclei vary from 1/10,000 to 1/100,000 of the radii of atoms. The unit of atom size is the angstrom (1 A = 10^{-8} cm), whereas the unit of nuclear size is the fermi (1 f = 10^{-13} cm).

Various types of experiment have provided R_0 values of 1.2 to 1.5 f. Using $R_0 = 1.4$ f, we can calculate the radius of Br^{80} to be

$$R = (1.4 \times 10^{-13})\,(80^{1/3}) = (1.4 \times 10^{-13})\,(4.3) = 6.0 \times 10^{-13} \text{cm} = 6.0 \text{ f}$$

For U^{238}, the calculation of the radius gives

$$R = (1.4 \times 10^{-13})\,(238^{1/3}) = (1.4 \times 10^{-13})\,(8.4)$$

$$= 11.8 \times 10^{-13} \text{ cm} = 11.8 \text{ f}$$

From these two calculations, we see that the radius only doubles in size when the mass number triples in value.

1–6   Nuclear Coulomb Barrier

The packing of neutrons and protons into the nucleus causes it to have a certain physical extension or size as discussed in the last section. The presence of the protons also causes it to have a positive charge. The basis for the successful interpretation of the Rutherford scattering experiment was the repulsion of the dipositive alpha particles by this positive charge of the nucleus.

Physicists speak of the repulsive force between the nucleus and the approaching positively charged particle as the **nuclear coulombic barrier.** According to the equation expressing the energy of repulsion between two bodies of like charge, the coulomb barrier energy should be equal to the product of the two charges divided by the distance between their centers. Therefore, by Coulomb's law,

$$V = \frac{(Ze)_1 (Ze)_2}{D} \qquad (1\text{–}4)$$

where Z is the atomic number and e the unit protonic charge (4.8×10^{-10} esu). If we use this value of e and express D in centimeters, V has the dimensions of ergs.

As an example, let us consider an alpha particle just in contact with a U^{238} nucleus and calculate the coulombic repulsion energy, i.e., the height of the coulomb barrier for U^{238} to alpha particles at a distance equal to the sum of their radii.

$$V = \frac{Z_1 Z_2 e^2}{R_U + R_{He}} = \frac{(92 \times 2)\,(4.8 \times 10^{-10})^2}{(1.4 \times 10^{-13})\,[(238^{1/3}) + (4^{1/3})]}$$

$$= 3.88 \times 10^{-5} \, \text{erg}$$

Since the erg is not a convenient unit in nuclear physics, the result is always given in MeV after multiplication by the conversion factor 6.24×10^5.

$$V = (3.88 \times 10^{-5} \, \text{erg})\,(6.24 \times 10^5) = 24.2 \, \text{MeV}$$

According to the principles of classical mechanics, the alpha particle would require a kinetic energy of at least 24.2 MeV in order to approach close enough to make contact with the U^{238} nucleus. With less kinetic energy, it could not overcome the barrier and would be repulsed before contact. Classically, then, coulomb barriers are impenetrable. However, nuclei do not obey perfectly the principles of classical mechanics and the nuclear coulomb barrier is not completely impenetrable to lower-energy particles. For such "quantum-mechanical" barriers, there is some probability that lower energy alpha particles will "tunnel" through the barrier and reach the U^{238} nucleus. This probability increases as the kinetic energy approaches 24.2 MeV. The nuclear coulomb barrier may be represented as a potential energy hill of the shape illustrated in Fig. 1–4.

According to the diagram in Fig. 1–4, when the particle is less than a nuclear radius distance from the center of the nucleus, the repulsive coulomb barrier is abruptly cut off and the particle falls into a nuclear potential energy well. This means that if the particle should penetrate or climb over the barrier to get inside the

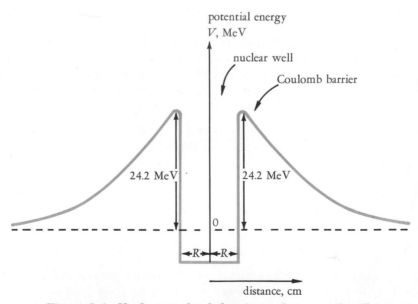

Figure 1–4 Nuclear coulomb barrier and potential well for U^{238} and He^4.

nucleus, it is held very tightly within the nucleus by the nucleons already present.

1-7   Nuclear Forces

The nuclear potential well in Fig. 1–4 must mean that there are forces holding together the nucleons in a nucleus. Furthermore, these forces must be stronger than the proton coulombic repulsion forces present since nucleons *do* stick together to form stable nuclei. A full understanding of the basic nature of these nuclear forces is essential to any theoretical attempt to describe the nucleus. Unfortunately, a complete understanding has eluded nuclear physicists thus far. Nevertheless, many characteristics of these nuclear forces have been observed in a wide variety of experiments. We are all familiar with the other basic forces—gravitational and coulombic; a brief discussion of the properties of this third type will serve to show wherein it differs from the first two.

From Fig. 1–4 we learn that nuclear forces are *short range*. They are much weaker than the repulsive coulomb force at distances greater than the nuclear radius. However, at a distance close to R the nuclear forces are felt abruptly and the coulomb repulsion is overcome. Precise measurements indicate that the distance over which the nuclear force is felt is of the order of 1 f. This means that in a nucleus containing many nucleons, nuclear attractive forces will exist only between those nucleons that are immediately adjacent. Now we can understand why BE/A is roughly constant. If each nucleon in a nucleus shared nuclear forces with all the other nucleons present, the total attractive force (binding energy) would be proportional to $A(A - 1)$ or approximately A^2 and BE/A^2 would then be almost constant. However, if nuclear forces are shared only by adjacent nucleons, the total attractive force will be proportional to the total number of nucleons and BE/A will be almost constant, the latter being the observed relationship.

The second major characteristic of nuclear forces is that they are *charge-independent*. The nuclear force of attraction is the same between two protons, two neutrons, or a neutron and a proton. However, between two protons there is also present the coulombic repulsive force and it decreases slightly the net attractive force. Experimentally, this charge-independent character is demonstrated by the scattering of both neutrons and protons from hydrogen gas. When the proton scattering is corrected for coulombic repulsion, the extent of scattering resulting from nuclear force effects is almost identical for both neutrons and protons.

It has already been mentioned that an acceptably quantitative theory of nuclear forces has not yet been formulated. In 1937 a Japanese physicist, H. Yukawa, set forth a theory that attempted to explain nuclear forces as the result of an exchange of an unknown particle between adjacent nucleons. The two nucleons theoretically experience an attractive force because they share the exchanging particle. This postulate resembles somewhat the explanation of the covalent chemical bond, in which electrons participate in the exchange forces by being shared by two atoms. Yukawa calculated that this nuclear exchange particle must have a mass approximately 200 times that of an electron. Two years later a subatomic particle was discovered and named the **muon** or the **mu meson**. It had a mass equal to 210 electron masses and seemed to be Yukawa's exchange particle. In 1947 the **pion (pi meson)** with a mass equal to 273 electron masses were discovered. Since pions interact strongly with nucleons whereas muons do not, it is now believed that the former are the Yukawa exchange particles.

SUMMARY

When new phenomena are observed by scientists, attempts to explain them frequently utilize ideas and principles that have effectively led to an understanding of other scientific observations. Generally these principles are based on the system of classical mechanics developed by Isaac Newton and many others. For the physical world directly apprehensible through our senses, this technique has been successful, since the macroscopic world obeys the precepts of classical mechanics. The world of the atom and the nucleus, however, is a submicroscopic world that differs in many important ways from the environment in direct physical contact with our senses. Consequently, the technique of trying to explain these submicroscopic systems by means of models (i.e., pictures) from the macroscopic systems of classical mechanics cannot be expected to be very satisfactory; e.g., we mentioned earlier that a nuclear coulomb barrier in classical mechanics would be impenetrable to low-energy particles, whereas experimentally we can observe that occasional penetration by such particles does occur.

In the case of the atom, the original Rutherford model was based on classical mechanics but failed to explain why the electrons would not spiral into the nucleus as they should in a classical system. Bohr, in an arbitrary manner, postulated that this did not occur for the reasons that the system was not perfectly classical and atomic electrons existed in stable energy levels. The final step was taken for the atom when all attempts to include classical mechanics were rejected and a new type of mechanics—quantum mechanics— was employed. We now realize that quantum mechanics governs the behavior of all physical objects whether they be atoms or universes. However, for objects larger than atoms, quantum mechanics and classical mechanics predict the same behavior; therefore the latter, being mathematically more simple, is used. In the atom, the forces involved between the individual electrons and between the electrons and the nucleus are the familiar coulomb electrostatic forces. Furthermore, the electrons are relatively far from each other and from the central, heavy nucleus. For these situations physicists have been able to progress very far toward a thorough understanding of atoms and molecules.

The nucleus, however, is a closely packed and very dense body with a repulsive coulomb force between the protons and a strong, short-range nuclear force between adjacent nucleons. Consequently, the attempt to explain nuclear phenomena by analogy to familiar physical models is doomed to very limited success. This limitation makes the task of establishing a comprehensive and satisfactory theory of the internal structure and behavior of the nucleus extremely difficult. It will be necessary to gather and correlate a great deal more experimental data before such a theory can be expected. This inherent limitation of present nuclear models should be kept in mind in trying to understand the discussions in this and successive chapters.

PROBLEMS

1. Calculate the total binding energy for $_{20}Ca^{40}$ and for Pu^{239}. $M_{Ca^{40}} = 39.9751$; $M_{Pu^{239}} = 239.1262$

Ans: $Ca^{40} = 342$ MeV

2. Calculate the binding energy per nucleon in Ca^{40} and in Pu^{239}. *Ans: $Ca^{40} = 8.55$ MeV*

3. If the decay energy for alpha decay of Pu^{239} is 5.24 MeV, what is the mass of U^{235}?

$M_{He^4} = 4.0039$ *Ans:* 235.1167

4. Calculate the radii of the following nuclei using $R_0 = 1.4 \times 10^{-13}$ cm: He^4, O^{16}, Fe^{56}, As^{75}, Cd^{112}, Ho^{165}, Pb^{206}, U^{238}, and Fm^{256}.   *Ans:* $Cd^{112} = 6.75 \times 10^{-13}$ cm

5. Plot the radius values calculated in the preceding problem as a function of mass number and discuss the resulting curve.

6. Calculate the coulomb barrier of a U^{238} nucleus to a proton when they are just in contact.   *Ans:* 13.1 *MeV*

7. List two major characteristics of nuclear forces and describe how these characteristics cause the nuclear forces to differ from the coulombic forces in atoms.

8. The density of metallic aluminum is 2.7 g/cm³. Calculate the density of the Al^{27} nucleus, using $R_0 = 1.4$ f and $M_{Al^{27}} = 27.0$, and compare the result with the 2.7 g/cm³ for the ion in the metallic lattice.

II

Radioactivity

RUTHERFORD AND SODDY were the first to suggest that radioactivity was due to spontaneous transformations of one element into another; nature, by radioactivity, was accomplishing the goal of the alchemists. Although chemical transformations can be very drastically affected by conditions of temperature, pressure, physical state, etc., it was discovered that these did not affect radioactive transformations. Chemical reactions occur by rearrangements of outer electrons, whereas radioactive changes originate in the nucleus. Since binding energies and reaction energies are so much greater for the nucleus than for ordinary chemical and physical changes, it is not surprising that nuclear transformations are unaffected by ordinary environmental conditions.

NUCLEAR STABILITY

Perhaps the most important observation about radioactivity is that some nuclides are radioactive and others are not. Why is C^{12} stable to radioactive transformation, whereas a C^{14} atom changes spontaneously into an atom of N^{14}? In Sec. 1–7 we discussed nuclear forces briefly and pointed out that the best evidence for their existence is the fact that some nuclides are stable. The presence of protons in close proximity to each other in nuclei gives rise to strong, disruptive coulomb forces of repulsion. The nuclear forces in stable nuclei are sufficient to overcome this disruptive force and to produce in the nucleus an over-all attractive binding force. Conversely, in unstable nuclei there is a net imbalance between the different forces.

2–1 Neutron-to-Proton Ratio

The greater the number of protons, the greater the total coulombic instability. If neutrons are present, they result in a stronger total nuclear force since the net nuclear force is proportional to the total number of nucleons (recall from Sec. 1–4 that $BE \propto A$). However, the presence of too many neutrons may sometimes decrease the stability of the nucleus for reasons discussed in Sec. 6–2. Consequently, there are ratios of neutrons to protons that provide maximum stability to nuclei. For elements at the beginning of the periodic table, it is found that stability is best achieved by equal numbers of protons and neutrons. Helium-4, carbon-12, oxygen-16, and neon-20 are a few examples of this stability for a neutron-to-proton (n/p) ratio of unity. As Z increases, so also do the repulsive coulomb forces. To overcome this, the total nuclear force must be increased by the addition of more neutrons; thus the n/p ratio increases above unity and reaches a value of 1.5 at Bi^{209}. The value of n/p necessary for stability for any element is not unique but often covers a small range. Elements of odd Z usually have only one or two stable isotopes, whereas elements of even Z may have several stable isotopes; consequently, the range of n/p values is greater for elements having even atomic numbers. For example, tin $(Z = 50)$ has stable isotopes ranging from $A = 112$ to $A = 124$. The stable n/p range for tin is 1.24 to 1.48. However, the adjacent elements of odd Z, indium $(Z = 49)$ and antimony $(Z = 51)$, have ranges of 1.31 to 1.35 and 1.37 to 1.41, respectively.

2–2 Abundance of Nuclear Types

The comparison between the number of stable isotopes that tin has and the number that indium and antimony have reflects another fact: stability is enhanced by even numbers of protons and/or neutrons. $_{50}$Sn has ten stable isotopes; $_{48}$Cd and $_{52}$Te each have eight. On the other hand, $_{47}$Ag, $_{49}$In, and $_{51}$Sb each have two, and $_{45}$Rh and $_{53}$I each have only one. The stable isotope of $_{53}$I has 74 neutrons, that of $_{45}$Rh has 58, those of $_{49}$In have 64 and 66, etc. Notice that there is no stable nuclide in this group that has both Z and N odd. In fact, in all the stable elements only nine cases are known of stable nuclei with both odd Z and odd N. Four of these nuclei have quite low values of A—$_1$H^1, $_3$Li^6, $_5$B^{10}, and $_7$N^{14}. The remaining five—$_{19}$K^{40}, $_{23}$V^{50}, $_{57}$La^{138}, $_{71}$Lu^{176}, and $_{73}$Ta^{180}—have very low isotopic abundances. For example, only 0.24 per cent of the vanadium atoms found in nature have $A = 50$; the other 99.76 per cent have $A = 51$. Table 2–1 characterizes the stable nuclei by Z and N and reflects the great preference of nature for even N and even Z numbers.

The greater stability of nuclei with even numbers of protons and neutrons is explained in terms of the stabilization gained by the combination of like nucleons into pairs, just as electrons of opposite spin pair in atoms and molecules. If a nucleus has, for example, an even number of protons, all these protons can exist in pairs. However, if the nucleus has an odd number of protons, at least one of these protons must exist in an unpaired state. The increase in stability resulting from complete pairing in elements of even Z is responsible for their ability to accommodate a greater range in neutron number, as discussed earlier for tin relative to indium and antimony.

Observe also that stable isobars (nuclei with the same value of A but different values of Z) must be different by at least two

Table 2–1

Type	Number
odd N–odd Z	9
odd N–even Z	56
even N–odd Z	53
even N–even Z	165

units in Z. $_{30}Zn^{64}$ and $_{28}Ni^{64}$ are stable isotopes of zinc and nickel but $_{29}Cu^{64}$, an isobar of Zn^{64} and Ni^{64}, is not stable.

ALPHA DECAY

It was shown soon after Becquerel's discovery that there were three types of emissions from radioactive atoms, α, β, and γ rays (Fig. 2–1).

2–3 Characteristics of Alpha Decay

Nuclides emitting alpha particles decrease in A by four units and in Z by two since the alpha particle is a helium nucleus.

$$_{92}U^{238} \rightarrow {}_{90}Th^{234} + {}_{2}He^4$$

or

$$_{92}U^{238} \xrightarrow{\alpha} {}_{90}Th^{234}$$

Alpha radioactivity has been observed for all the elements above lead in the periodic table and for several nuclides as light as $_{60}Nd^{144}$ and $_{62}Sm^{146}$. The alpha particles usually have between 3 and 9 MeV of kinetic energy but, since they are relatively massive

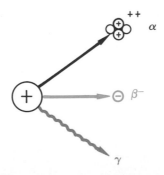

Figure 2–1   Three types of nuclear radiation.   Alpha rays are composed of helium nuclei, beta rays of electrons; gamma rays are electromagnetic radiation (not particles).

and doubly charged, they do not penetrate very far into matter. A thick sheet of paper is sufficient to stop completely the alpha particles emitted in radioactive decay. Another characteristic of alpha decay is that the alpha particles have discrete energies. If U^{238} is placed in an instrument that can count the number of alphas emitted at different energies, a plot similar to that in Fig. 2–2 is obtained. For U^{238}, 77 per cent of the alpha particles emitted have 4.18 MeV of energy and 23 per cent have 4.13 MeV. In the alpha decay of U^{238}, alpha particles of 4.18-MeV kinetic energy are observed experimentally, although the Q value of the reaction is 4.27 MeV; the Th^{234} atom carries off the difference, i.e., 0.09 MeV. The **law of conservation of momentum** requires that the Th^{234} remove 4/238 of the kinetic energy and that the He^4 remove 234/238 of it, in perfect agreement with the 0.09 and 4.18-MeV values.

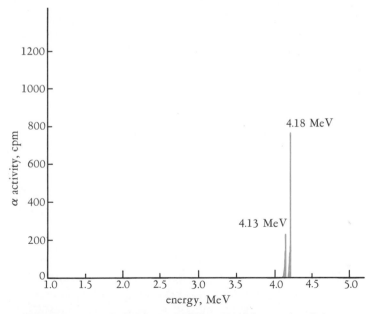

Figure 2–2 Distribution of alpha particles emitted from U^{238} plotted as a function of their energies.

2–4   Alpha-Particle Tunneling

One aspect of alpha decay that puzzled physicists for a long time was how alpha particles of less than 10 MeV energy could get out of the nucleus. In Sec. 1–6 we calculated that the coulomb barrier to penetration of U^{238} by an alpha particle is about 24.2 MeV. For an alpha particle to leave the U^{238} nucleus, classical mechanics would require it to possess at least 23.7 MeV (the coulomb barrier for $Th^{234} + He^4$), yet the particles have less than 5 MeV. The theory of alpha decay developed by Gamow, Guerney, and Condon pointed out that this is not a classical barrier but rather a quantum-mechanical barrier, through which low-energy alphas *could* occasionally tunnel. The probability of such tunneling is very low— for the 23.7-MeV barrier, the 4.18-MeV alphas of U^{238} have only one chance in 10^{38} and that would seem quite negligible. However, we can consider in a simple picture that the alpha particle is bouncing around in the nucleus. In this simple picture, the energy of the alpha particle and the size of the nuclear diameter are such that the particle hits the surface approximately 10^{21} times per sec. We can, therefore, calculate the time necessary to establish a probability of unity for tunneling. If the probability of emission P is 1, then the time t is

$$t = P \times \frac{\text{number of sec per hit}}{\text{probability of tunneling per hit}} = 1 \times \frac{10^{-21}}{10^{-38}} = 10^{17} \text{ sec}$$
$$= 3 \times 10^9 \text{ years} \qquad (2\text{-}1)$$

This calculation predicts the average lifetime of the U^{238} nucleus to be about 3×10^9 years before alpha decay.

BETA DECAY

2–5   Negatron Emission

A second general type of radioactive transformation is known as beta decay. If the n/p ratio of the nucleus is too large for stability, a more stable situation can be approached by a change that will reduce the n/p value. This can be done by either reducing the number of neutrons or increasing the number of protons. Actually the nucleus does both by ejecting an electron, formed by the transformation of a neutron to a proton. This reaction can be represented

$$n \rightarrow p^+ + e^-$$

and is known as **negatron decay** or, simply, as **negative beta decay.** The result is an increase in Z by one unit with no change in A; e.g.,

$$_{49}\text{In}^{116} \rightarrow {}_{50}\text{Sn}^{116} + {}_{-1}\beta^0$$

2–6 Beta-Decay Energy

Although there is no change in mass number, there is a change in mass in beta decay. In these spontaneous, exothermic processes, the heavier nuclide decays to the lighter with the decrease in mass appearing principally as the kinetic energy of the products. Since it is very improbable that two adjacent isobars would have exactly the same mass, the heavier would decay to the lighter. This provides us with a simple explanation of the rule on the stability of adjacent isobars mentioned in the previous section. The In^{116} reaction may be rewritten to indicate the energy change

$$_{49}\text{In}^{116} \rightarrow {}_{50}\text{Sn}^{116} + {}_{-1}\beta^0 + Q$$

If Q represents the decay energy and M the atomic masses,

$$Q = 931 \, (M_{\text{In}^{116}} - M_{\text{Sn}^{116}}) = 931 \, (115.94096 - 115.93779)$$

$$= 931 \, (0.00317) = 2.95 \text{ MeV}$$

The mass of the electron is not included in the calculation. Since atomic masses are used, it is necessary to be certain that the number of atomic electrons on the two sides of the equation for the energy-mass calculation is balanced. In^{116} has 49 electrons; therefore its atomic mass includes *the In^{116} nuclear mass* plus *the mass of 49 electrons* minus *the total binding energy of these 49 electrons.* Sn^{116} has 50 electrons and its atomic mass includes *the Sn^{116} nuclear mass* plus *the mass of 50 electrons* minus *the total electronic binding energy.* The equation is properly concerned with the changes in nuclear mass between In^{116} and Sn^{116}, so when atomic masses are used the Sn^{116} mass has one electron too many for direct calculation. (The difference in the total electronic binding energies is negligible for this calculation.) The correct calculation would thus be

$$Q = 931 \, [M_{\text{In}^{116}} - (M_{\text{Sn}^{116}} - M_{e^-}) - M_{\beta^-}]$$

Since $M_{e^-} = M_{\beta^-}$ these last two terms cancel out, and the actual calculation involves only the In^{116} and Sn^{116} atomic masses.

The 2.95 MeV of decay energy would be expected to be carried off as kinetic translational energy by the Sn^{116} and the beta particle (electron). The energy would be distributed between the two in inverse proportion to their masses. Since the Sn^{116} is very much more massive than the electron, the latter is expected to carry off essentially all the decay energy.

2-7   Beta-Energy Spectrum

When the number of alpha particles from U^{238} decay was plotted as a function of their energies, we saw that they had either 4.13 or 4.18 MeV of kinetic energy. Since alpha particles are emitted with discrete energies, such a plot shows a line spectrum analogous to the atomic line spectrum observed when chemical elements emit visible light after excitation. If the number of electrons from beta decay is plotted as a function of their energies,

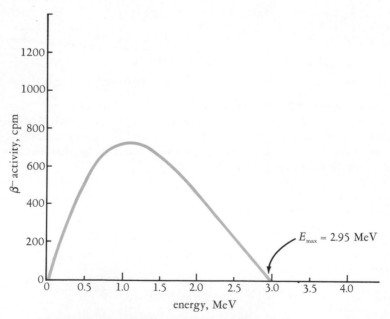

Figure 2–3   **Distribution of the negatron decay activity of In^{116} plotted as a function of the energies of the negative beta particles.**

a curve like that shown in Fig. 2–3 is observed. There are no discrete, sharp peaks as in alpha decay; rather, there is a broad, continuous distribution of energies, extending from almost zero to some maximum value. We have calculated that 2.95 MeV of energy should be associated with the beta decay of In^{116}, and Fig. 2–3 shows this to be the value of the maximum energy. However, very few of the electrons have this maximum energy; the average beta-particle energy is approximately one-third the 2.95-MeV calculated decay energy. Since the beta decay of In^{116} to Sn^{116} must be accompanied by the loss of 2.95 MeV, a way must be found to account for the removal of a good part of this energy in most emissions by some means other than the electron. Wolfgang Pauli in 1931 suggested that the missing energy is carried off by a particle that is very difficult to detect. Enrico Fermi used this concept in his theory of beta decay and named this particle of almost zero mass and no charge the neutrino ("little neutral one"). Approximately 25 years after the original suggestion, this particle was actually detected and shown to have the properties predicted by Fermi. Thus, in the In^{116} decay, when a beta particle of 1.00 MeV is emitted, a neutrino of 1.95 MeV is emitted simultaneously.

2–8   *Positron Emission and Electron Capture*

If negative beta-particle emission occurs for nuclei with n/p values too large for stability, then a reverse process might be expected to occur for nuclei with n/p values too small for stability. These latter have a deficiency of neutrons and an excess of protons, so the decay change should convert a proton to a neutron. As in negatron decay, this process may have to be repeated in several consecutive steps before a stable n/p value is obtained.

The conversion of a proton to a neutron can occur in two different ways—either by emission of a positron (**positive beta decay,** where the reaction is $p^+ \rightarrow n + \beta^+$) or by absorption of an electron, usually from the K or L shells of the atom (**electron capture,** where the reaction is $p^+ + e^- \rightarrow n$). Two such reactions are

$$_{51}Sb^{120} \rightarrow {}_{50}Sn^{120} + \beta^+$$

and

$$_{79}Au^{195} \xrightarrow{\text{E.C.}} {}_{78}Pt^{195}$$

Positive beta decay and electron capture are competing processes, with the probability of electron capture increasing as Z increases. With few exceptions, unstable neutron-deficient nuclei with values of Z below 30 undergo positron decay, whereas such nuclei with Z values above 80 decay most often by electron capture. Both processes are observed for $30 < Z < 80$.

The positron is identical to the electron except that it posesses a positive charge. Again, as in negatron decay, positrons are emitted with a continuous spectrum of energies and with the simultaneous ejection of a neutrino.

2–9   Rules for Decay Calculations

By considering the calculations for the negatron decay of In^{116} (Sec. 2–6) and for the positron decay of Sb^{120} (Problem 9), it is possible to formulate some simple rules for the calculation of nuclear decay energies when atomic masses are used.

1. In equations involving negatron decay, electron capture, or alpha decay, it is not necessary to add or subtract electron masses.

2. In equations involving positron emission, it is necessary to subtract two electron masses from the difference between the masses of the initial and the product nuclei.

3. It is not necessary to add electron masses in equations for nuclear reactions induced by charged particles or neutrons.

GAMMA DECAY

Nuclei emit a third type of radiation, gamma rays, and these cause no change in either Z or A. Gamma rays are electromagnetic radiation like X rays, ultraviolet and visible light, and radio waves. Having no charge or rest (zero-energy) mass, gamma rays do not produce a change in Z or A in the emitting nucleus, but they do cause a decrease in mass corresponding to the energy carried away by the gamma ray. Frequently alpha or beta decay leaves the nucleus in an excited state, and this excitation energy is removed by gamma-ray emission. For example, in the decay of U^{238}, 77 per cent of the alpha particles have 4.18 MeV and 23 per cent

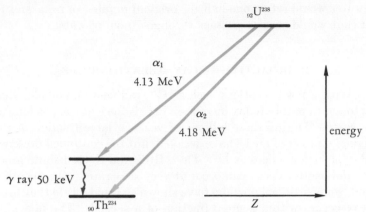

Figure 2–4 Energy relationships in the decay of U²³⁸ to Th²³⁴. Alpha particles of 4.18 and 4.13 MeV and a gamma ray of 0.05 MeV are observed.

have 4.13 MeV of energy. Obviously, decay by emission of 4.13-MeV alpha particles leaves the nucleus with 0.05 MeV greater energy than do 4.18-MeV alpha emissions. It is found experimentally that this 0.05 MeV is carried off by ejection of a gamma ray of that energy. We can represent this schematically by the diagram in Fig. 2–4.

In the great majority of cases, the emission of gamma rays occurs immediately after alpha or beta decay. In some instances, however, the nucleus may remain in the higher energy state for a measurable length of time. In such a case, the nuclide is said to have an **isomeric state.**

Gamma rays are emitted with a discrete energy, like alpha particles, rather than with a continuous spectrum of energies as negatron and positron decay particles are. Since they have no mass or charge, gamma rays do not interact readily with matter and therefore possess great penetrating power. Whereas a 4-MeV alpha particle is stopped by a film of water a few millimeters thick, a 4-MeV electron requires approximately 2 cm of water to stop it. By contrast, a beam of 4-MeV gamma rays passing through 20 cm of water would retain one-half the original number of rays, and 10 per cent would survive passage through 70 cm of water.

With a few exceptions such as C^{14}, radioactive nuclides that are found in nature today have been in existence at least as long as the earth. During these billions of years, a large fraction of the original number of nuclei have decayed, but the continued presence today of such nuclides as U^{238}, Th^{232}, Rb^{87}, and K^{40} is definite proof that radioactive decay can occur at very slow rates. On the other hand, some artificial nuclides have shown so rapid a rate that total decay occurs within a small fraction of a second. The nonexistence in nature of elements with $Z > 92$ is explained by the fact that all the isotopes of these elements have lifetimes considerably shorter than the age of the earth.

2–10   Equations for Radioactive Decay

Radioactive decay is a random process—among 1000 atoms capable of undergoing decay it is not possible to identify which will be the next to do so. Experiment has shown that the decay rate is directly proportional to the number of active atoms present. If 10,000 atoms show a decay rate of 5 atoms per min, then 50,000 of the same atoms show a decay rate of 25 atoms per min.

A (disintegrations/min) $\propto$ N (number of atoms)

Therefore

$$A = \lambda N \qquad (2\text{-}2)$$

The proportionality constant λ is known as the decay constant and is a characteristic of the nuclide decaying. Another simple expression of considerable use is the relationship between the number of atoms N_t present at time t and the number originally present N_0 (i.e., $t = 0$). Equation (2–2) can be written $dN/dt = \lambda N$, and upon integration this gives

$$N_t = N_0 e^{-\lambda t} \qquad (2\text{-}3)$$

or

$$\log N_t = \log N_0 - \frac{\lambda t}{2.3}$$

From Eq. (2–2) it is easy to see that Eq. (2–3) can also be written

$$A_t = A_0 e^{-\lambda t} \tag{2-4}$$

or

$$\log A_t = \log A_0 - \frac{\lambda t}{2.3}$$

Eq. (2–3) can be used to prove that the time required for one-half the number of radioactive atoms present to decay is constant. If it takes an hour for 20,000 atoms to decay to 10,000 atoms, half of the remaining 10,000 atoms will decay in the second hour, half of the remaining 5000 atoms will decay in the third hour, etc. This time for 50 per cent decay is known as the half-life of the nuclide. Thus I^{131} is shown in Fig. 2–5 to have a half-life of 8.06 days. From Eq. (2–4) we find for 50 per cent decay

$$\frac{A}{A_0} = 0.5 = e^{-\lambda t_{1/2}}$$

$$\lambda t_{1/2} = -2.303 \log 0.5 = 2.303 \log 2 = 0.693$$

$$t_{1/2} = 0.693/\lambda \tag{2-5}$$

or

$$\lambda = 0.693/t_{1/2}$$

The half-life (and, of course, the decay constant) is a definitive characteristic of a radioactive species since it is unlikely that any two nuclides will have exactly the same half-lives; nor will the half-life be affected by the physical or chemical state of the radioactive atom. Consequently, knowledge of the decay energies and the half-life is often sufficient to allow identification of a nuclide as to Z and A by use of nuclear data tables. U^{238} has a $t_{1/2}$ of 4.5×10^9 years and alpha energies of 4.18 MeV (77 per cent) and 4.13 MeV (23 per cent). A radioactive sample with these characteristics is almost certainly U^{238} as there is no other nuclide yet known with these properties.

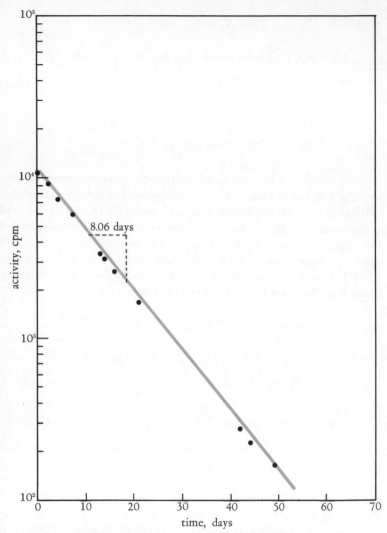

Figure 2–5 The logarithm of the activity plotted as a function of time for a sample of I[131]. The half-life is 8.06 days.

2–11   Natural Radioactivity

Four families of radioactive nuclides have been discovered for the elements of $Z > 82$, the $4n + 3$, $4n + 2$, $4n + 1$, and $4n$ families. The existence of four (and only four) families is a simple consequence of the fact that only alpha decay (reducing A by 4) and beta decay (no change in A) occur between these elements. To classify nuclear species by family, the mass number is divided by 4. Thus for U^{238}, $238/4 = 59 + 2$, placing U^{238} in the $4n + 2$ family. In fact, U^{238} is the first naturally occurring member of the $4n + 2$ family. Th^{232} has this distinction for the $4n$ family and U^{235} for the $4n + 3$ family. The $4n + 1$ family is not found in nature because the longest-lived member is Np^{237} with a half-life of only 2.2×10^6 years—too short to allow its existence in nature today. Since alpha decay changes A by 4 units and beta decay leaves A unchanged, there is no change in family with either alpha or beta decay. Th^{234}, the decay product of U^{238}, is also in the $4n + 2$ family, the decay chain of which is shown in Fig. 2–6.

2–12   Parent-Daughter Relation

In a radioactive decay, the emitting nucleus is known as the **parent** and the residual nucleus as the **daughter.** Thus, in Fig. 2–6, U^{238} is the parent and Th^{234} the daughter; in turn, Th^{234} is the parent of Pa^{234}, etc. For these nuclides as well as for all the other cases where the daughter is radioactive, it is of interest to know the characteristic pattern of growth and decay of the daughter activity.

Case 1: If the parent has a shorter $t_{1/2}$ than the daughter, the daughter activity will grow to some maximum value and then decay at its own half-life rate, as shown in Fig. 2–7.

Case 2: If the parent is longer-lived than the daughter, the daughter activity will grow to a maximum value and then decay at the half-life rate of the parent (Fig. 2–8). It cannot decay at its own half-life rate since the parent is constantly adding more daughter in accord with the parent half-life. This condition is known as **transient equilibrium** although in the strict sense it is a steady state and not a true equilibrium. Of course, if the

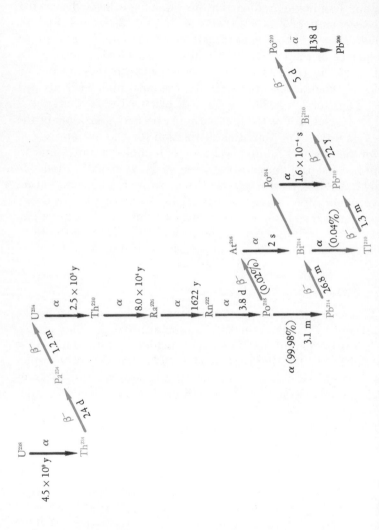

Figure 2–6 The decay sequence of the $4n + 2$ family of natural radioactivities. Nuclides that decay predominantly by alpha decay are in gray, those by beta decay in color.

32

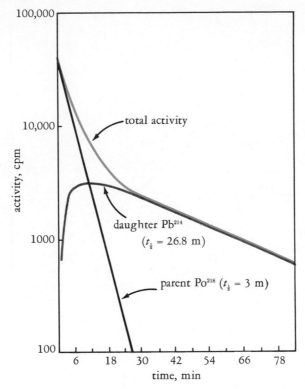

Figure 2–7   Growth and decay curves for the parent-daughter pair Po²¹⁸ $\xrightarrow{\alpha}$ Pb²¹⁴.

daughter is chemically separated from the parent, the decay rate of the former will follow the daughter half-life.

Case 3: If the parent has such a long life that there is no detectable change in the decay rate of the parent during the period of observation, the daughter activity will grow to a maximum and then remain constant as long as the daughter is not separated from the parent (Fig. 2–9). This extreme situation is known as **secular equilibrium.** It can be shown that the activity rates of parent and daughter are equal at the steady state; i.e.,

$$A_1 = A_2$$

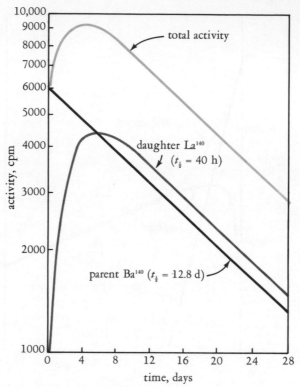

Figure 2–8   Growth and decay curves for the Ba^{140} → La^{140} system, reflecting transient equilibrium.

For uranium ore that has not been chemically affected for several million years, so that equilibrium has been established throughout the $4n + 2$ chain,

$$A_{U^{238}} = A_{Th^{234}} = A_{Pa^{234}} = A_{U^{234}} = A_{Th^{230}} \text{ etc.}$$

Since $A = \lambda N$,

$$(\lambda N)_{U^{238}} = (\lambda N)_{U^{234}}$$

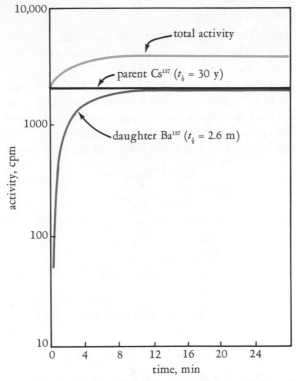

Figure 2–9   Growth and decay curves for the Cs^{137} → Ba^{137} system, reflecting secular equilibrium.

From this relationship we can calculate the expected isotopic abundance of U^{234} in uranium ore.

$$\frac{N_{234}}{N_{238}} = \frac{\lambda_{238}}{\lambda_{234}} = \frac{\text{half-life}_{234}}{\text{half-life}_{238}} = \frac{2.5 \times 10^5 \text{ years}}{4.5 \times 10^9 \text{ years}}$$

Therefore

$$\frac{N_{234}}{N_{238}} = 5.6 \times 10^{-5}$$

Since uranium ore is 99.28 per cent U^{238}, the expected isotopic abundance of U^{234} is 0.0056 per cent.   The experimental value is exactly this.

2-13 Age of the Earth

It is possible to use the naturally occurring nuclides to estimate the age of the elements on earth. U^{238} has a half-life of $4.5 \times$
10^9 years, whereas that of U^{235} is 7.1×10^8 years. Today the isotopic abundance of uranium is 99.28 per cent U^{238} and 0.72 per
cent U^{235}. If we assume that initially these isotopes were in equal
abundance and that no isotopic separation has occurred through
physical or chemical changes, the abundance ratio reflects the
shorter half-life of U^{235}. If t is the time of decay, then

$$N_{235} = N_{0235}e^{-\lambda_{235}t}$$

and

$$N_{238} = N_{0238}e^{-\lambda_{238}t}$$

Our basic assumption is that $N_{0235} = N_{0238}$; therefore

$$\frac{e^{-\lambda_{238}t}}{e^{-\lambda_{235}t}} = \frac{N_{238}}{N_{235}} = \frac{99.28}{0.72} = 138$$

$$e^{-(\lambda_{238}-\lambda_{235})t} = 138$$

Thus

$$-(\lambda_{238} - \lambda_{235})t = 2.303 \log 138 = 4.91$$

Since

$$\lambda_{238} = 0.693/t_{1/2} = 1.54 \times 10^{-10} \text{ year}^{-1}$$

$$\lambda_{235} = 0.693/t_{1/2} = 9.76 \times 10^{-10} \text{ year}^{-1}$$

then

$$t = \frac{4.91}{8.22 \times 10^{-10}} \approx 6 \times 10^9 \text{ years}$$

This calculation estimates the age of the elements on earth to be
about 6 billion years, subject to the assumption that equal amounts
of U^{235} and U^{238} were initially present. It is fairly safe to assume,
since U^{235} is an even-odd nucleus whereas U^{238} is an even-even one,
that the initial concentration of U^{235} was no greater than that of
U^{238} and that 6 billion years represents an upper limit on the age of
the earth.

Technicium, promethium, and the transuranium elements are
not found in nature since all of the possible isotopes of these elements have half-lives much shorter than the age of the earth. The
prohibition on stability for both of a pair of neighboring isobars

prevents the stability of any isotopes of technicium and promethium, even for n/p values expected to provide stability. The stable n/p value for technetium, e.g., should be approximately 1.28, predicting stability for Tc^{97} and for Tc^{99}; Tc^{98} is a nuclide of odd N and odd Z and therefore its stability is less probable. Molybdenum has stable isotopes of $A = 92, 94-98$, and 100; ruthenium has stable isotopes of $A = 96, 98-102$, and 104. The stability of Mo^{97}, Mo^{98}, Ru^{98}, and Ru^{99} in particular precludes the possibility of stability for the most likely technicium isotopes, Tc^{97}, Tc^{98}, and Tc^{99}.

SUMMARY

The types of radioactive decay are listed in Table 2–2 along with the characteristics of the emitted radiation and the consequences to the emitting nucleus.

Alpha particles are emitted in groups with discrete energies that vary between 3 and 9 MeV, depending on the emitting nuclide. Beta particles, either negatron or positron, are emitted with a continuous spread of energies whose maximum coincides with the calculated decay energy. The most penetrating radiation, gamma rays, are emitted like alpha particles in discrete energy groups. Despite the large total number of known nuclides, natural and artificial, knowledge of both the mode and the energy of radioactive decay serves to provide almost certain identification in many cases.

Table 2–2
Radioactive Decay

	Radiation		Change in nucleus	
Type	Mass number	Charge	Mass number	Atomic number
α	4	+2	decreases by 4	decreases by 2
β^-	0	−1	no change	increases by 1
β^+	0	+1	no change	decreases by 1
E.C.			no change	decreases by 1
γ	0	0	no change	no change

PROBLEMS

1. Why is it necessary, as A increases, for the n/p values to increase above unity in order to maintain nuclear stability?

2. What is the explanation for the emission of 4.2-MeV alpha particles by U^{238} when the coulomb barrier to this emission is 23.7 MeV?

3. From the masses of Am^{242} and Cm^{242}, decide which is beta-unstable (β^- for Am^{242} or E.C. for Cm^{242}) and calculate the beta-decay energy.

$M_{Am}{}^{242} = 242.1344$; $M_{Cm}{}^{242} = 242.1338$ *Ans:* 0.56 *MeV*

4. Br^{80} has two isomeric states. The higher energy state decays by gamma emission with a decay energy of 0.086 MeV. The ground state undergoes beta decay to Kr^{80} with a beta-decay energy of 2.00 MeV. If the mass of Kr^{80} is 79.9425 amu, calculate the masses of the two isomers of Br^{80}.   *Ans:* $Br^{80g} = 79.9446$

5. What is the alpha activity in disintegrations per min for a 1-mg sample of Pu^{239} ($t_{1/2} = 24,300$ years)?

Ans: 1.43 $\times$ 10^5 *dpm*

6. If a sample of Pm^{147} has an activity of 10^7 disintegrations per sec, what is the amount of Pm^{147} in the sample?

Ans: 0.3 *µg*

7. If a sample of Y^{90} has an activity of 10^6 disintegrations per min, what will its activity be 2 weeks later? ($t_{1/2}$ of $Y^{90} = 64$ hours)

Ans: 2.7 $\times$ 10^4 *dpm*

8. For the decay chain $Ce^{144} \xrightarrow{\beta^-} Pr^{144} \xrightarrow{\beta^-} Nd^{144}$, when the Ce^{144} and Pr^{144} are in secular equilibrium, what is the weight of Pr^{144} per gram of Ce^{144}?   *Ans:* 0.042 mg

9. Use the β^+ decay of Sb^{120} to Sn^{120} to show that two electron masses must be subtracted from the difference in atomic masses to calculate β^+-decay energies. Then calculate the $Q_{\beta}{}^+$ if $M_{Sb}{}^{120} = 119.94138$ and $M_{Sn}{}^{120} = 119.93860$.   *Ans:* 1.57 *MeV*

10. Use a periodic chart to calculate the average stable n/p ratios for $Z = 1, 5, 10, 15, 20, 30, 40, 50, 60, 70,$ and 80. Plot the number of neutrons vs. the number of protons and draw a smooth curve through the points. Starting at $Z = 1$, also draw a straight line with a slope of unity, i.e., $n/p = 1$. Compare the two plots.

III

Detection of Radiation

W HEN THE RADIATIONS from radioactive decay pass through matter, they interact with the atoms and molecules in the matter and by this interaction lose their energy. Since the nucleus occupies such a small portion of the total volume of an atom, it is not surprising that in the great majority of these interactions the extranuclear electrons are more directly involved than is the nucleus.

3–1 Interaction of Radiation with Matter

As radiation—alpha, beta, or gamma—passes an atom, it can transfer some of its energy to the atom. In certain cases the amount of energy transferred is sufficient to cause an electron to escape from the atom altogether, and ionization results. The positive ion and the electron are known as an **ion pair** (see Fig. 3–1). Frequently the electrons from this primary ionization have sufficiently high kinetic energies to cause secondary ionization in other atoms. Although the number of electrons produced in secondary ionization is often larger than that from the primary ionization, the average kinetic energies of these secondary electrons are lower than those of the primary electrons. In many inter-

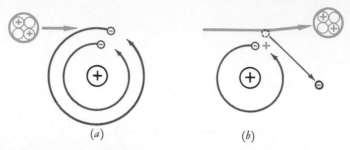

Figure 3–1   Formation of an ion pair: (a) alpha particle approaches an orbital electron and (b) causes it to leave the atom, producing an ion pair.

actions, the initial radiation transfers insufficient energy to the atom to cause ionization. Instead, an electron is raised to a higher, excited energy level though it is still retained by the atom. Atoms thus excited return to lower energy states by emission of electromagnetic radiation such as X rays, visible light, etc. (see Fig. 3–2). The electrons emitted by the higher-energy ionization interactions, being of lower average energy than the initial radiation, often cause excitation rather than ionization in the secondary interactions.

Although atoms have been discussed, the same processes of ionization and excitation occur for molecules. Molecules that are excited to higher energy states can also de-excite by emission of electromagnetic radiation, often in the visible- or near-visible-wavelength region of the spectrum (fluorescence). De-excitation may occur alternatively by transfer of the energy in collisions with other molecules or by dissociation of the molecule into such fragments as atoms, smaller molecules, ions, and radicals. Consequently, the initial effect of the interaction of radiation with molecules is to produce, depending upon the complexity of the molecules, a variety of molecular fragments in the form of ions and radicals.

The primary ions and radicals interact to produce new ions and radicals as well as neutral molecules. In many instances the

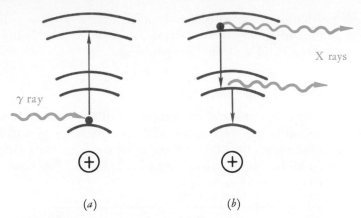

(a)   *(b)*

Figure 3–2 Fluorescence: (a) the gamma ray excites the electron to jump to a higher energy level; (b) the electron falls back to the original level in two steps, with X rays or visible light emitted in each step.

positive ions are neutralized by recombination with a secondary electron. Ion-molecule reactions occur quite generally and may be represented

$$AB^+ + CD = AC^+ + BD$$

In solids and liquids these secondary processes take place in the immediate vicinity of the primary ionization or excitation, and the over-all effects are dependent on the type (e.g., alpha vs. gamma) and the energy of the radiation. In gases, the low density allows sufficient diffusion that recombination may take place at relatively large distances from the original interaction site. In solutions, the effect of the solvent as well as that of the solute must be considered. For example, radiation acts on water to produce hydrogen peroxide, a product that may chemically reduce or oxidize a solute depending on the over-all nature of the solution. The study of the many chemical reactions that take place among the ions, radicals, and molecules of a chemical system upon exposure to radiation constitutes the field of radiation chemistry. In nuclear chemistry we are more concerned with the nucleus and with nuclear radiations than with the chemical effects of these radiations on the surroundings; however, use is made of these chemical effects to detect and measure the radiations.

3-2 Energy Loss per Ion Pair

The many experimental measurements of the number of ion pairs produced in gases by alpha and beta particles of various energies have shown that the average energy loss by the particle is about 34 eV for each ion pair formed. Table 3-1 lists some of

Table 3-1

Gas	Particle	Average energy loss, eV
air	alpha	35.0
air	beta	34.0
hydrogen	alpha	36.3
hydrogen	beta	36.3
methane	alpha	29.2
methane	beta	27.3

these values. This 34-eV average loss is quite small compared to the initial energy of most radiations, the latter being of the order of 10^6 eV. As a consequence, many ion pairs are produced in the passage of a single alpha, beta, or gamma particle through matter.

3-3 Alpha Particles

Alpha particles emitted by radioactive nuclides in the majority of cases have energies between 4 and 9 MeV. Po^{212} emits alphas of 8.95 MeV, whereas those from U^{238} have energies of 4.18 and 4.13 MeV. Since the alpha particles are so much heavier than electrons, they are deflected very slightly when their coulomb fields interact with atoms or molecules to form ion pairs. As a result, alpha particles travel in a straight line as they pass through matter. As mentioned in Sec. 2-3, in solids or liquids the total length of this path is quite short. However, in gases at standard temperature and pressure the path is several centimeters in length.

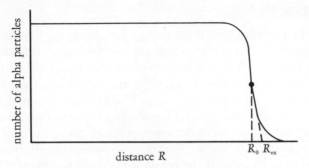

Figure 3–3   **Number of alpha particles plotted as a function of distance from their source.** R_0 **is the range calculated from the value of** R **at the inflection point on the range curve;** R_{ex} **is the range obtained from a line tangent to the curve at the inflection point.**

The range in air for alpha particles with an initial energy E (MeV) can be calculated from

$$R(\text{cm}) = 0.309 \, E^{3/2} \tag{3-1}$$

Fig. 3–3 is a plot of the number of alpha particles at various distances from the source; this is known as a range curve. As expected, the number of particles remains almost constant until very near the end of the range. The lack of an abrupt cutoff in the range curve shows that the alpha particles do not all have exactly the same path lengths; there is a slight variation or straggling. This straggling arises from statistical fluctuations not only in the energy loss per ion pair about the 34 eV average value but also in the number of encounters per unit of path length.

The alpha particle decreases in velocity as it loses its energy, taking progressively longer to pass through each successive interval of range. The longer time spent increases the probability of interaction. The expected result is that there should then be a steady increase in the number of ion pairs formed, rather than a constant density of ion pairs along the path length. Experimentally it is found that the number of ion pairs do indeed increase as the velocity decreases.

3-4   Beta Particles

Beta particles lose their energy by the same mechanism as alpha particles. However, there are several important additional complications. Since the masses of the beta particle and of the orbital electrons are equivalent, the former can lose a large fraction of its energy in a single collision. The beta particle undergoes a wide-angle deflection in such a collision; consequently, beta particles are scattered out of the beam path all along its length (Fig. 3-4). The energetic ionized electron will cause extensive secondary ion pair formation with the result that again the average energy loss, considering all the ion pairs, is about 34 eV. The secondary ionization, in fact, provides 70 to 80 per cent of the total ionization in beta processes.

For the same initial energy, beta particles have a very much greater velocity than have alpha particles since the electronic mass is approximately 1/7300 of the helium mass. This greater velocity results in a correspondingly lower specific ionization and, consequently, in a much longer range. Furthermore, when an electron passes near a nucleus, it may be deflected by the positively charged nuclear field. In such a fast-moving, very light particle, this deflection causes a loss of energy by emission of **bremsstrahlung** (braking radiation) or low-energy X rays. The loss of energy by

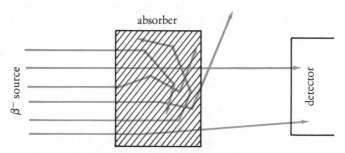

Figure 3-4   Scattering of beta particles in an absorber, illustrating that the range measured by the detector is not a measure of the total path traveled by the electrons because of the wide-angle deflections.

radiation increases with the beta energy and with the atomic number of the, absorber material. In aluminum, approximately 1 per cent of the energy of a 1-MeV electron is lost by radiation and 99 per cent by ionization, whereas in lead the loss by radiation is about 10 per cent.

A range curve for beta particles has a quite different shape than has the curve for alpha particles. The continuous spread in energies (Sec. 2–7) plus the extensive wide-angle scattering of the beta particles accounts for the fact that range curves for betas continuously decrease. Even for a beam of initially monoenergetic electrons, the continuous removal of electrons from the beam path by wide-angle deflections would result in a plot showing a continuous decrease in electron numbers with distance. Since approximately 95 per cent of the original beta particles are stopped in the first half of the range, it is more common to speak of the absorber thickness necessary to stop 50 per cent of the particles than to

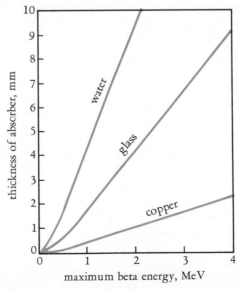

Figure 3–5   Plot of absorber thicknesses required to stop beta rays completely.

speak of the range: this half-thickness value is also much easier to
ascertain experimentally than is an apparent range. Fig. 3–5 plots
the range in various absorbing materials as a function of maximum
beta energy.

3–5 Gamma Rays

Gamma rays are electromagnetic radiation as are X rays,
light, radio waves, etc. They are very penetrating and, being uncharged, they have a very low ionization per unit of path length.
The number of ion pairs produced in a given path length by gamma
rays is only 1 to 10 per cent of that produced by beta particles of
the same energy. Consequently, the ionization is almost completely secondary, resulting from the action of a few high-energy,
primary ion pairs. Unlike alpha and beta particles, which lose
their energy as a result of many collisions, gamma rays are completely stopped in one or two interactions. Since a gamma ray
may be removed from the beam in the first few angstroms of its
length or may travel several inches with no interaction at all and
then be removed, it is not possible to apply the range concept to
gamma rays in the way that it is applied to alpha particles. However, as in the case of beta particles, it is experimentally easy to
measure the thickness of absorber necessary to remove half of the
initial gamma rays from a beam. Fig. 3–6 shows the required half-
thicknesses of a number of materials for different gamma ray
energies.

There are three modes of interaction whereby gamma rays
lose their energy. The first is known as the **photoelectric effect.**
The gamma ray is absorbed completely by the atom (or molecule)
as a whole and, since this excites the atom above its ionization
potential, an electron is ejected. The ejected **photoelectron**
carries off the excitation energy minus the ionization energy, so
that the energy of the photoelectron is expressed

$$E_{e^-} = E_\gamma - \text{I.P.} \qquad (3\text{–}2)$$

where I.P. is the ionization potential (binding energy) of the
electron. If the photoelectron originates from an inner electronic
shell, then an electron from a higher energy level falls down to fill

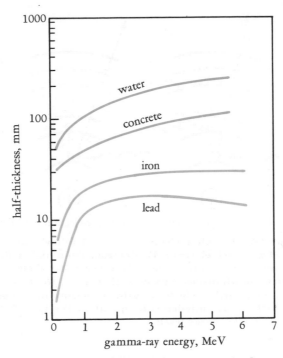

**Figure 3-6   Plot of absorber thicknesses required to reduce
gamma-ray intensity to one-half the original intensity.**

the hole.   This results in emission of X rays and even of low-
energy electrons known as **Auger electrons.**   The process of
electron cascade accompanied by X-ray and Auger-electron emission is continued until the atom is reduced to its minimum (ground-
state) energy.   (Fig. 3–7 shows a possible sequence of events in a
schematic way.)   In turn, the photo- and Auger electrons as well
as the X rays cause extensive secondary ionization.

The energy of the gamma rays is often great enough that,
rather than interacting with the whole atom, the gamma ray
interacts with an orbital electron directly.   This is called the
Compton effect or **Compton scattering** after A. H. Compton,
the American physicist who discovered it.   Upon interaction, the

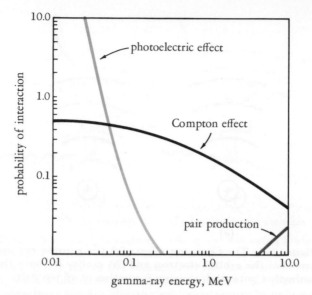

Figure 3–9   Curves showing the probabilities in aluminum absorber of the three types of gamma-ray interaction as a function of gamma-ray energy.

keV in lead.   Between 60 keV and 15 MeV in aluminum and between 600 keV and 5 MeV in lead, the principal mode of interaction is the Compton effect.   Pair production predominates in the energy range above that for the Compton effect.   In Fig. 3–9, the probabilities for the three modes of interaction in aluminum are shown as a function of gamma-ray energy.

DETECTOR TECHNIQUES

The excitation and ionization produced by radiation in solids, liquids, and gases is used in a variety of techniques to detect and measure the radiation.   The type and energy of the radiation as well as its intensity may be ascertained. We shall consider briefly the most common of those detection techniques.

3–6   Photographic Emulsions

The oldest technique for radiation detection utilizes photographic emulsions.   Henri Becquerel, a French physicist, observed in 1896 that samples of uranium ore possessed the ability to darken photographic plates even when layers of cardboard and

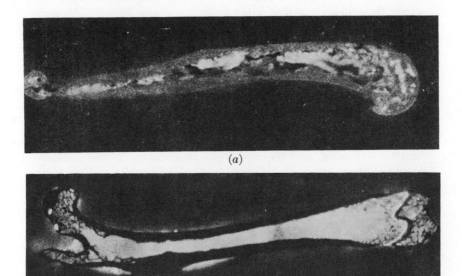

(a)

(b)

Figure 3–10   Radioautographs of C^{14} in rat's bone: (a) C^{14} accumulated both in the bone and in its marrow following injection of the rat with $NaHC^*O_3$; (b) C^{14} accumulated only in the marrow following injection of the rat with a C^{14}-labeled dye.   From *Scientific American*, *193*, 39 (1955); courtesy of Dr. A. Lindenbaum and Argonne National Laboratory, Argonne, Illinois.

paper were placed between the ore sample and the plate. The observation of this phenomenon was the first indication of the existence of radioactivity.

Nuclear radiation exposes photographic film in the same manner as visible light. By exciting the silver halide as it passes through, radiation increases the sensitivity of the silver halide to reduction by the developing agent. Consequently, the sensitized silver halide grains are reduced to silver more rapidly than are the unsensitized grains and appear as dark areas in the developed film. If the emitting substance is placed in a thick photographic emulsion, alpha particles produce short and thick dark tracks because their energy is dissipated within a short range; beta and gamma rays produce much longer, thin tracks since their specific ionizations are so much lower. The intensity and length of the track can often be used to identify the type of radiation and, in an approximate fashion, the energy. The number of tracks or the total darkening can be used to measure the rate of radioactive decay.

By radioautography, the distribution of a radionuclide in a substance can be measured. The substance is laid on a photographic emulsion, and the radiation reproduces on the film an image of the position and density of the radionuclide. Fig. 3–10 shows a radioautograph of the distribution of carbon-14 in bone. Structural defect detectors often use photographic film to measure the relative intensity of radiation after passage through various sections of a piece of metal or other material.

3–7   Cloud and Bubble Chambers

If a gas that is saturated with water vapor has its temperature lowered, condensation of liquid water normally occurs. However, in the absence of dust particles or other pieces of foreign material to serve as centers for condensation initiation, the cooled gas may exist in a state of supersaturation. Such a state is not very stable and condensation of the excess water vapor is rapid once initiated. The passage of ionization through a supersaturated vapor produces ion pairs along the path of the radiation, and these ion pairs can serve as condensation centers. Consequently, in such a vapor,

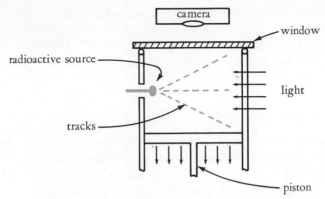

Figure 3–11 Schematic diagram of a Wilson cloud chamber in operation.

the track of ionizing radiation is marked by the appearance of small droplets of fog. In a cloud chamber, the pressure on a saturated vapor is decreased rapidly, producing a decrease in temperature upon expansion. Tracks caused by alpha particles will be relatively short, straight, and thick compared to the longer, thinner, and wandering tracks from beta rays; the differences in type of track are the result of the differences in range and in ionization per unit of path length. By placing the cloud chamber in a magnetic field, the alpha and beta tracks can be made to deflect in opposite directions. Fig. 3–11 is a schematic diagram of a simple cloud chamber.

One disadvantage of the cloud chamber is the low density of the vapor. High-energy radiations may have ranges quite beyond the dimensions of a practical chamber. This disadvantage is overcome in the bubble chamber wherein a liquid—usually liquid hydrogen—is kept at its boiling point. Upon a slight reduction in pressure, bubbles form at the sites of the ion pairs produced along the path of an ionizing radiation. The greater density of the liquid as compared with the vapor results in shorter ranges and increases the probability of interaction within the chamber for such events as ion-pair formation by a high-energy gamma ray.

Very large bubble chambers are in use today—some as large as 6 ft in diameter. The complications of operating and maintaining a liquid hydrogen bubble chamber are increased by the low temperatures necessary and by the dangers inherent in the use of hydrogen (Fig. 3-12).

3-8   Ionization Counters

In most work with radionuclides, it is desirable to have a means of immediate detection and measurement of the radiation. Detectors filled with gas have been found to fill this need in a satisfactory fashion. If the gas is placed between two electrodes of opposite sign, the electrons and the cations of the ion pairs produced by the radiation as it traverses the gas are attracted to opposite electrodes. With small potential differences between the two electrodes, the ion pairs are not separated very rapidly and extensive recombination can occur. However, as the potential difference is increased, the electrons and cations separate more rapidly, reducing the probability of recombination. Eventually a voltage is reached at which recombination is negligible; essentially all the electrons are collected at the anode and all the cations at the cathode. Each ion carries 1.6×10^{-19} coulomb. Therefore, for the 4.18-MeV alphas from U^{238} that form 1.18×10^5 ion pairs per alpha particle, the collected charge is

$$Q = (1.18 \times 10^5)(1.6 \times 10^{-19}) = 1.9 \times 10^{-14} \text{ coulomb}$$

A detector that operates in the fashion described is termed an **ionization chamber** (Fig. 3-13). These are relatively simple and inexpensive detectors, though rugged and reliable. The electrode voltages are only several hundred volts. However, the collected charge is quite small and must be magnified by electronic amplification, with the result that the cost and complexity of the total counting system are increased.

3-9   Proportional Counters

If the potential difference between the two detector electrodes is increased beyond the value required to reach a constant count

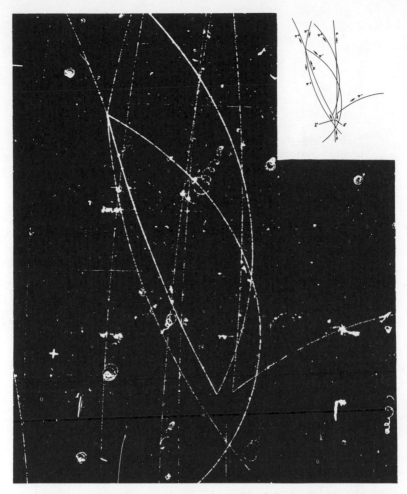

Figure 3-12   First example of antilambda production in
the 72-inch hydrogen bubble chamber.   The antiproton
from decay of the antilambda was annihilated with a target
proton to produce four charged pions.   Lambda and pion
particles are mesons.   Antiparticles have opposite charges
but the same masses as corresponding normal particles.
From *Physical Review*, 121, 1789 (1961).

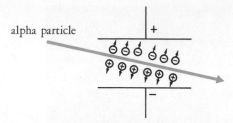

alpha particle

**Figure 3-13   Ion-pair formation in the counting gas of a
parallel-plate ionization chamber.**

rate with an ionization chamber, the electrons are accelerated
with increasing kinetic energy away from the site of ion-pair production and toward the anode.   Eventually, this increases the
collected charge above the constant value observed in the voltage
region used for ionization chamber operation.   The electrons have
acquired sufficient kinetic energy at these voltages to cause secondary ionization in the gas molecules that they strike in their
passage to the anode (Fig. 3-14).   Since the charge collected is the
sum of the charges of all free electrons present, this secondary
ionization provides a multiplication of the collected charge.

In proportional counters, the collected charge is 10^3 to 10^5

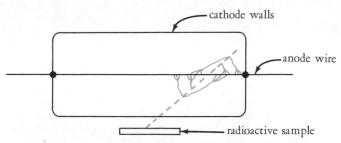

cathode walls

anode wire

radioactive sample

**Figure 3-14   Localized electron multiplication at the cen-
ter anode wire in a proportional counter.**

times as large as in an ionization chamber. Furthermore, the collected charge is directly proportional to the extent of primary ionization. Since the latter is a function of the type of radiation and its energy, proportional counters are used to distinguish between alphas and betas and to measure the energies of these particles. Gamma rays have such a low probability of interaction in gases that the efficiency of their detection is very low in any gas-filled detector.

3-10 Geiger-Müller Counters

In the voltage region used for operation of Geiger-Müller counters, the kinetic energy of the primary electrons is so great that considerable kinetic energy is imparted to the secondary electrons. Collected by the counter-wire, the electrons are sufficiently energetic that they cause emission of photoelectrons from the wire. These photoelectrons in turn produce more secondary electrons. The process goes on until an "avalanche" of electrons spreads along the whole length of the wire. This results in the simultaneous formation of a sheath of slow-moving, positive ions along its entire length, reducing the potential-field gradient near the wire enough to prevent further ionization. No new counts are measurable until the positive-ion sheath has drifted far enough away from the counter wire to permit re-establishment of the high potential-field gradient necessary for multiplication. Consequently, a G.M. detector cannot handle as high counting rates as can a proportional counter. In the latter, since the avalanche is localized, charge multiplication and collection can occur at other sites on the wire even while part of the wire is insensitive.

A single ion pair is sufficient to initiate the avalanche in a G.M. detector. Since all radiations produce total-charge pulses of the same size, G.M. detectors cannot be used to differentiate directly between alphas, betas, or gammas, nor can energy measurements be made. Geiger tubes multiply the primary charge by a factor of approximately 10^8. Since the collected charge is rather large, the complexity of the auxiliary equipment required is considerably reduced (Fig. 3-15).

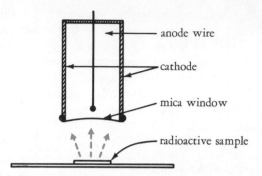

**Figure 3-15   Counting arrangement for an end-window
Geiger counting tube.**

3-11   Scintillation Counting

For gamma rays it is desirable to use a detector of high density
so as to increase the probability of capture within the detector
volume.   Inorganic crystals that have the property of luminescence are most useful for gamma-ray measurements.   After energy
absorption has excited the ions or molecules of a crystal to elevated
energy states, their decay back to lower levels and finally to the
ground state results in the emission of radiant energy having a
wavelength in the visible or near-visible region of the spectrum.
This scintillation passes through the crystal and enters a photomultiplier tube (Fig. 3–16) in which the photon of light causes the
emission of electrons.   These photoelectrons are accelerated to
electrodes where they cause the emission of more electrons.   This
process of electron multiplication is continued through perhaps
ten stages, so that the total multiplication is greater than 10^8.

Sodium iodide crystals containing small amounts of thallium
are in common use for gamma detection.   Anthracene is often used
for beta measurements, and zinc sulfide is sometimes used for
detecting alpha particles.   Such scintillating substances as *p*-
terphenyl may be dissolved in xylene to provide liquid scintillating
systems.   The latter are used particularly for counting low-energy
beta-emitting nuclides such as C^{14} and H^3.

A scintillation counting system is more expensive than a G.M.

aluminum metal jacket   dynode stages in photomultiplier tube

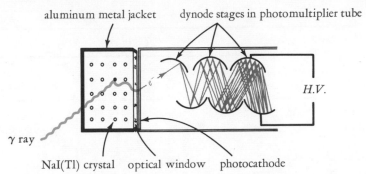

H.V.

γ ray

NaI(Tl) crystal   optical window   photocathode

Figure 3–16   A scintillation crystal with a photomulti-plier tube.   For simplicity, an electron multiplication (gain) of two at each dynode stage is shown; in practice, the gain is eight to ten per stage, with as many as ten dynode stages.

counting system since more amplification and better voltage stability are necessary.   However, a scintillation counter can handle much higher count rates than can a G.M. counter.   Its greatest advantage lies in the ability of a scintillation counter to determine very precisely the energy of gamma rays, a measurement not readily possible by other means.

SUMMARY

All counting systems are based on the effects of the interaction of radiation with matter.   In gas-filled detectors, radiation produces ionization in the gas, and both electrons and positive ions are accelerated to electrodes.   Their collection at the electrodes permits the electronic system to record a count.   In inorganic and organic scintillation crystals, radiation causes emission of photons that are detected by photomultiplier tubes, again permitting registration of a count.   Table 3–2 is a resumé of the counting systems discussed in this chapter.

A description of more sophisticated nuclear radiation measuring systems is beyond the scope of this book.   Multichannel

Table 3-2

	Counter			
	Ionization chamber	*Proportional*	*G.M.*	*Scintillation*
Normal detection state	gas	gas	gas	liquid or solid
Radiation usually counted	α, β	α, β	α, β, γ	α, β, γ
Multiplication of primary charge	1	10^4	10^8	10^8
Complexity of total system	medium	high	low	high
Particular advantages	simplicity; measurement of alpha energies	high count rates	simplicity; adaptability	high count rates; measurement of gamma energies

analyzers, magnetic beta-ray spectrometers, and time-of-flight spectrometers are only a few of the many other instruments available. The rich diversity of the instrumentation used in nuclear science—for detection, counting, and analysis of type and energy of radiation—reflects its scientific scope and the imagination of nuclear scientists and adds considerable zest to research in this field. An important development of the last few years that well illustrates this diversity is the utilization of **solid-state counters** prepared from semiconductor silicon used in transistors.

PROBLEMS

1. If the average loss per ion pair in a gas is 34 eV, how many ion pairs are formed in the gas by a 5.4-MeV alpha particle?

Ans: 1.6×10^5

2. Why does secondary ionization provide so much larger a percentage of the total ionization for beta particles than for alpha particles?

3. What are *bremsstrahlung?*

4. Explain the difference between the photoelectric effect and the Compton effect.

5. For many nuclides listed as gamma emitters, electrons of almost the same energy as the gamma ray as well as low-energy X rays and electrons are often observed experimentally. Explain the origin of both groups of electrons and of the X rays.

6. Describe the operation of a proportional counter.

7. Describe the operation of a Geiger-Müller counter.

8. Consult the *Journal of Chemical Education* for discussions on radioactivity detection techniques. Prepare a short report on solid-state (i.e., semiconductor) counters.

IV

Fission

4-1 Spontaneous Fission

A mode of spontaneous radioactive decay in addition to alpha, beta, and gamma emission is known.   This new mode of decay is a very violent one; it causes the nucleus to break into two roughly equal parts while at the same time ejecting several neutrons.   Only the heaviest elements show this **spontaneous fission** decay.   Whereas alpha decay is first found for the naturally occurring nuclides in the lead region, spontaneous fission decay is first observable in the thorium region.   A half-life of greater than 10^{21} years has been reported for Th^{232}, so long a period that its measurement is extremely difficult.   However, spontaneous fission half-lives decrease rapidly with Z: that of $_{92}U^{238}$ is 6×10^{15} years, that of $_{96}Cm^{244}$ is 1.4×10^7 years, and that of $_{100}Fm^{254}$ is 200 days.   Fig. 4-1 is a summary of spontaneous fission half-lives as a function of A for the elements from thorium to fermium.   The half-lives for spontaneous fission grow shorter much more rapidly with increasing Z than do the half-lives for alpha, beta, or electron capture decay.   The rapid increase in the spontaneous fission decay rate may, in fact, be the deciding factor in determining how many new elements can be made beyond $Z = 103$.

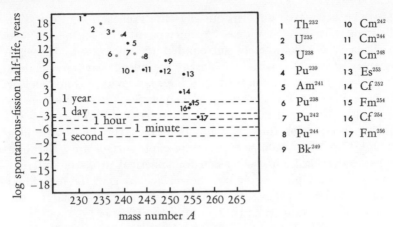

Figure 4–1   The half-life (partial) of spontaneous decay as a function of mass number A for some isotopes between $Z = 90$ and $Z = 100$.

4–2   The Liquid-Drop Model

In Sec. 2–1 we discussed briefly the two opposing forces whose balance or lack thereof decide the stability of a nucleus. The disruptive force results from the mutual repulsion of the protons present in the nucleus. This force increases as the number of protons increases and decreases as the distance between the protons increases. Each proton present repels the other $Z - 1$ protons in inverse proportion to the interproton distance d_{p-p}; thus the force of repulsion is expressed

$$\text{force of repulsion} \propto Z(Z - 1)/d_{p-p} \qquad (4\text{–}1)$$

In Sec. 1–5, we concluded that the nuclear radius is proportional to $A^{1/3}$. Since the radius is the direct sum of the internucleon distances,

$$d_{p-p} \propto A^{1/3}$$

As Z increases, $Z(Z - 1)$ approaches the value Z^2; therefore, for higher values of Z, Eq. (4–1) becomes

$$\text{coulomb repulsive force} \propto Z^2/A^{1/3} \qquad (4\text{–}2)$$

The attractive force in nuclei is the nuclear force operative between adjacent nucleons. A nucleon at the surface of the nucleus is not completely surrounded by nucleons and, consequently, does not experience as great a total nuclear force as does a nucleon inside the nucleus. To have as great a total nuclear force as possible, the nucleus must have as few surface nucleons as possible. The total nuclear force, then, resembles in some ways the surface-tension force of a liquid. The latter tends to pull a liquid drop into the shape of lowest possible surface area, that of a sphere; the total surface tension for spherical drops of different sizes is directly proportional to the surface areas of the individual drops. For a nucleus, the surface area is proportional to the square of the radius (i.e., to $A^{2/3}$), and therefore

$$\text{nuclear attractive force} \propto A^{2/3} \qquad (4\text{--}3)$$

The ratio between these two forces should be a measure of the instability of the charged nuclear "liquid drop." This ratio is

$$\text{instability} \propto (Z^2/A^{1/3})/A^{2/3} \approx Z^2/A \qquad (4\text{--}4)$$

Obviously, with increasing mass the nuclei are increasingly less stable since Z^2 increases more rapidly than does A. From Fig. 1–3 it is possible to conclude that nuclei with A greater than 60 have a net instability. This means that their repulsive coulomb force is greater than the nuclear force. The repulsive force can be reduced if the nuclear charge is divided between two smaller nuclei. Although this division also reduces the total nuclear attractive force, the Z^2 dependence of the repulsive coulomb force causes the latter to be reduced by a greater relative amount. In order for fission to occur, it is necessary that the two fragments surmount a potential-energy barrier, as discussed in Chap. II for the emission of alpha particles. This barrier is similar to the activation-energy barrier that can prevent the occurrence of an exothermic chemical reaction unless the molecules have a minimum threshold kinetic energy. The fission barrier is sufficiently high to prevent nuclei from having spontaneous fission half-lives short enough to be observed experimentally until the thorium region ($Z = 90$) is reached. Consequently, instability to fission becomes observable when the value of Z^2/A exceeds 35.

In 1939, shortly after the discovery of fission, Niels Bohr, the Danish physicist who first proposed the quantum model of the atom in 1916, and John A. Wheeler, a young American physicist, offered an explanation of fission based on this analogy between the nucleus and a small liquid drop. Their description followed the concepts of the previous paragraphs. Let us summarize these ideas in a qualitative way. According to Bohr and Wheeler, a nucleus behaves somewhat like a small drop of incompressible liquid. The surface tension of such a drop tends to pull it into a spherical shape. If the drop is given extra energy, this energy causes distortions away from the spherical shape by reason of the kinetic motions of the molecules in the drop. Consequently, the drop oscillates between spherical and nonspherical shapes. If there is sufficient excitation energy, the drop occasionally oscillates into a very distorted shape from which the surface energy is unable to restore it. In such a case, the drop breaks into two parts, i.e., it undergoes fission. The nucleus is pictured as oscillating in the same way between spherical and distorted shapes as a result of the competition between the repulsive coulomb force and the attractive nuclear force. As the repulsive force increases, the probability of extreme distortion increases and with it the probability of fission. Thus, in nuclei below Th^{232} the repulsive force is sufficiently low that, if no extra excitation energy is added, the nucleus will oscillate into this fission shape too rarely for spontaneous fission decay to be observable. However, as Z^2/A increases, the frequency of occurrence of the fission shape increases and spontaneous fission becomes an observable mode of radioactive decay. Fig. 4–2 shows an oscillation sequence that leads to fission of the nuclear drop.

This liquid-drop model, in which the nucleus is treated as a

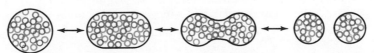

Figure 4–2 Liquid-drop model oscillations leading to fission.

compact assembly of nucleons, has been very useful. The nuclear energy states predicted from this model would be those associated with oscillations of the nucleus as a whole. In Chap. VI alternative nuclear models are discussed, in which the nuclear energy states are determined by individual nucleons. It is important to keep in mind that our basic understanding of the nucleus is inadequate at present to enable us to use a single nuclear model to explain all nuclear phenomena.

4–3   Induced Fission

The discovery that a nucleus could be made to undergo fission by bombardment with neutrons preceded that of spontaneous fission. Subsequent to the discovery of artificial radioactivity in 1934 by I. Curie (Madame Curie's daughter) and her husband, F. Joliot, research on nuclear reactions demonstrated that capture of a neutron by a nucleus in very many cases resulted in a product nucleus that was unstable to β^- decay. E. Fermi and others reasoned that if uranium were bombarded with neutrons, it might form the unknown element of atomic number 93 in accord with the sequence

$$_{92}U^A + _0n^1 \rightarrow _{92}U^{A+1} \rightarrow _{93}X^{A+1} + \beta^-$$

When this experiment was carried out in 1934, it was found that the product of the bombardment did emit β^- particles. Between 1934 and 1938, over 90 scientific articles were published describing research on the neutron bombardment of uranium; it was believed that elements with atomic numbers as high as 96 had been formed by several successive β^- decays. O. Hahn and F. Strassmann in Germany were among the many scientists prominent in this research area. In 1938 these two chemists concentrated their attention on the related possibility that capture of a high-energy neutron might result in immediate ejection of an alpha particle. The reaction in the case of uranium would be

$$_{92}U^A + _0n^1 \rightarrow _{90}Th^{A-3} + _2He^4$$

or, for thorium

$$_{90}Th^A + _0n^1 \rightarrow _{88}Ra^{A-3} + _2He^4$$

Extremely careful and painstaking chemical analysis convinced Hahn and Strassmann that the β-emitting products were not Ra, Ac, Th, or Pa, nor were they elements with $Z > 93$. Instead, they proved—to their own amazement—that radioactive isotopes of Sr, Y, Rb, Cs, Ba, and La were the sources of the β^- particles. In 1939 Hahn and Strassmann published these results, at the same time suggesting that these nuclides could be formed if the uranium nucleus divided into two large but not necessarily equal parts following neutron capture. Nuclear chemists and physicists immediately realized the error of their previous conclusions and the importance of the correct interpretation. Later in 1939 Bohr and Wheeler published their theory of the liquid-drop explanation of fission. The next year saw the discovery of spontaneous fission in uranium by the Russian physicists, G. N. Flerov and K. A. Petrzhak. Since 1939, it has been found that fission can be induced by many bombarding projectiles, among them gamma rays, neutrons, protons, deuterons, and alpha rays, as well as carbon, nitrogen, oxygen, and neon ions. Nuclei as light as the lanthanide (rare earth) elements have undergone fission as a result of high-energy bombardment.

4-4 Fission by Thermal Neutrons

To illustrate further the details of induced fission, let us consider the irradiation of uranium isotopes by neutrons. If a neutron has the same kinetic energy as a gas molecule at a given temperature, it is known as a thermal or slow neutron. The energies of these thermal neutrons are very low ($\ll 1$ eV) compared to the binding energy released by their capture in a nucleus. For U^{235} this binding energy is

$$_{92}U^{235} + {}_0n^1 \rightarrow {}_{92}U^{236}$$

$$Q = 931 \, (M_{U^{235}} + M_n - M_{U^{236}})$$

$$= 931 \, (235.1170 + 1.0090 - 236.1191)$$

$$= 931 \, (0.0069) = 6.4 \text{ MeV}$$

Consequently, the U^{236} nucleus is excited to 6.4 MeV. A similar calculation for U^{239}, formed by the capture of a thermal neutron by U^{238}, shows that its excitation energy is only 4.8 MeV. Experimentally, it is found that capture of a thermal neutron by U^{235} results in fission whereas capture of a thermal neutron by U^{238} does not. The conclusion to be drawn is that it must be necessary to add 5 to 6 MeV of excitation energy to uranium nuclei to cause fission. In other words, when 5 to 6 MeV extra energy is added to the disruptive coulomb force, the net distorting force sufficiently exceeds the nuclear attractive force that within a few oscillations the nuclear drop finds itself in a properly distorted shape to undergo fission. When the added energy is less than this, many more oscillations are necessary to permit the nucleus to assume a fissionable shape, and during this time the extra nuclear energy is emitted as a gamma ray, eliminating the chance of fission.

This reasoning can be tested by checking whether U^{238} will undergo fission upon neutron capture when the excitation energy is increased into this 5- to 6-MeV range. If a neutron of 1-MeV kinetic energy is captured, the excitation energy is $4.8 + 1.0 = 5.8$ MeV, a level that should be sufficient to cause fission. The proof of the theory is found in the fact that U^{238} does indeed undergo fission upon bombardment with 1-MeV neutrons.

There is no coulombic potential barrier for the neutron to overcome as it approaches the uranium nucleus since the neutron is uncharged. Therefore thermal neutrons can hit the nucleus even though their energy is quite small. Protons, however, have a coulomb barrier to their approach to a uranium nucleus. This barrier can be calculated by the method of Sec. 1–6 to be about 12 MeV. It has been mentioned several times that this is not an impenetrable barrier, and protons with less than 12 MeV of energy can occasionally leak through; nevertheless, although thermal neutrons cause fission of U^{235} and 1-MeV neutrons cause fission of U^{238}, proton-induced fission in uranium has quite a low probability of occurrence at bombarding energies below 6 to 8 MeV.

4–5   Energy of Fission

To calculate approximately the amount of energy released in fission, consider the splitting of U^{236} (from $U^{235} + n$) into two equal fragments of mass 118. The binding energy per nucleon in U^{236} is approximately 7.6 MeV whereas the binding energy per nucleon in nuclei of $A \approx 118$ is approximately 8.5 MeV. On the basis that the total binding energy of a nucleus is the energy released upon formation of the nucleus from its nucleons, the energy release in fission should be the difference between the total binding energy of the U^{236} and that of the two nuclei of mass 118. Therefore

$$E_f = \text{total } B.E._{U^{236}} - 2 \times \text{total } B.E._{M^{118}}$$

$$E_f = (236)(-7.6) - 2(118)(-8.5) = 210 \text{ MeV} \qquad (4\text{--}5)$$

Although this calculation is only approximate, experimentally the energy of fission is found to be about 200 MeV. It is this very large amount of energy released by fission that sets it apart as a nuclear process of great importance as a source of power.

Such a drastic process involving so much energy could be expected to be more complex than simple separation into two parts. Actually several neutrons as well as gamma rays are emitted in fission. The n/p ratio of uranium is substantially higher than are the stable n/p ratios of the fission-product nuclei. As a result there is a considerable neutron excess in the initial fission fragments, and several β^--decay steps are often necessary before the n/p ratio is adjusted to a more stable value. The total energy released in fission appears as the kinetic energies of the fission products and of the neutrons, as the energy of the fission gamma rays, and as the energy of radioactive (β^-) decay. An average energy distribution is given in Table 4–1 for fission involving U^{235} and a thermal neutron.

One of the first principles learned by all chemistry students is that of the conservation of mass and energy. Later it is learned that in balancing redox equations, charges must be balanced (conserved) on the

Table 4–1
Approximate Fission–Energy Balance

Kinetic energy of fission products	165 MeV
Kinetic energy of neutrons	5 MeV
Gamma-ray energy	15 MeV
Beta-decay energy	9 MeV
Total fission energy	194 MeV

two sides of each equation. Another quantity that is conserved in physical systems is momentum. If fission splits the nucleus into fragments of masses M_1 and M_2, the conservation of momentum $MV(V = \text{velocity})$ requires that

$$M_1 V_1 = M_2 V_2 \qquad (4\text{-}6)$$

Therefore

$$V_1/V_2 = M_2/M_1$$

From this relationship it is easy to show that

$$E_1/E_2 = M_2/M_1$$

If $M_2 > M_1$, this equation shows that $E_1 > E_2$; i.e., in an unequal fission split, the lighter fragment has a greater kinetic energy than the heavier fragment. (Compare with this the discussion in Chap. II on the energy of Th[234] and the alpha particle in U[238] decay.)

4-6   Mass Distribution in Fission

In Fig. 4–3 the observed distribution of kinetic energies from the fission of U[235] by thermal neutrons is shown. If most of the fission processes resulted in equal-sized fragments, then $M_1 \approx M_2$ and $E_2 \approx E_1$. From Fig. 4–3 it is obvious that E_2 is usually differ-

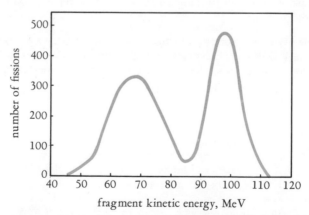

Figure 4–3   Kinetic-energy distribution of the fission fragments from the thermal neutron fission of U[235].

ent from E_1, thus the fission act must result in unequal splitting in the majority of cases. In fact, we can use Fig. 4–3 to estimate the mass ratio of the most probable fission products. Since $E_1 \approx 75$ MeV and $E_2 \approx 105$ MeV, M_2/M_1 (light/heavy) must approximate 0.7. If we assume that on the average two neutrons are lost in fission, then $M_1 + M_2 = 234$ (for $U^{235} + n$ fission). Now we have two equations with two unknowns and it is possible to solve for M_1 and M_2.

$$M_2/M_1 = 0.7$$

$$M_1 + M_2 = 234$$

Therefore $M_2 \approx 97$ and $M_1 \approx 137$. Combining these results with the curve in Fig. 4–3, we are led to expect that fission should be characterized by a double-humped distribution curve of fission-fragment masses, with one maximum around $A = 137$ and the other around $A = 97$. Fig 4–4 is such a curve and does show these expected maxima.

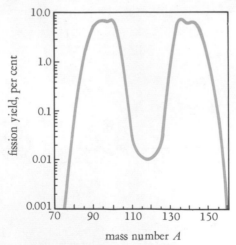

Figure 4–4 Mass distribution of the fission fragments from the thermal neutron fission of U^{235}.

4–7   *Symmetric vs. Asymmetric Fission*

It is believed that fission occurs in two different ways. One mode of fission favors equal-mass, or symmetric, splitting. The second mode favors unequal-mass, or asymmetric, splitting (Fig. 4–5). The symmetric and asymmetric modes compete with one another. In low-energy fission, such as the thermal neutron fission of U^{235} (Fig. 4–4), the asymmetric mode predominates. However, as the bombarding energy is increased, the symmetric mode becomes more important until at high energies the mass-yield distribution curve has only one maximum between $A = 97$ and $A = 137$. Fig. 4–6 shows the change in shape of the mass-yield curve for the fission of Np^{237} as the energy of bombarding alpha particles

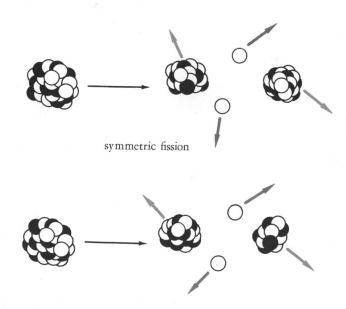

symmetric fission

asymmetric fission

Figure 4–5   Representations of the symmetric and asymmetric modes of fission. In both cases, two neutrons are shown being emitted during fission.

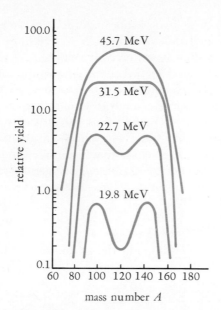

Figure 4–6   Mass distribution of the fission products from the bombardment of Np^{237} with alpha particles of 19.8, 22.7, 31.5, and 45.7 MeV.

is increased.   As expected, fission induced by high-energy bombardment results in a symmetric, single-humped mass-yield curve.

It takes great amounts of careful radiochemical work to obtain mass-yield curves since they require the separation of many nuclides in high degrees of purity and precise analyses of their absolute disintegration rates.   In this, as in almost every area of fission research, there is still much to be done before sufficient data are available to allow a thorough theoretical understanding of the complex nuclear process of fission.

NUCLEAR POWER

When U^{235} undergoes fission by capture of a thermal neutron, an average of 2.5 neutrons is released.   The neutrons from this

first fission can cause two or more additional fissions; they in turn
release enough neutrons to cause four to five more fissions; these
can cause eight to ten more, etc. If neutrons are prevented from
escaping the piece of U^{235} before causing fission, the first fission
initiates a rapidly expanding chain reaction. When a "critical
mass" of uranium—large enough to keep a chain reaction going—
is assembled, the number of fissions per unit of time rapidly increases. The result is the evolution of an almost unbelievable
amount of energy. If the chain reaction is allowed to grow uncon-
trolled, the evolution of energy becomes so great and so rapid that
an explosion occurs. This is the basis of the atomic bomb.

4–8   Nuclear Reactors

It is possible to assemble the uranium in a nuclear reactor
where the rate of the chain reaction can be controlled by materials
that absorb neutrons readily. The uranium is fabricated into
fuel elements and between these are inserted the **control rods,**
usually made of cadmium because of its exceedingly high absorption of neutrons. By inserting or withdrawing the control rods, the
number of neutrons present at any moment, and hence the fission
rate, can be kept constant. In order to prevent small explosions
or the melting of the fuel elements as a result of the accumulation
of released energy, the fuel elements are cooled by a flow of liquid
or gas. Water (H_2O) and heavy water (D_2O) are used as **coolants**
in many reactors. Very often the coolant also serves as the heat-
transfer medium whereby fission energy is transferred to a system
that can convert it to electricity for power use. Both U^{235} and
Pu^{239}, the two most commonly used "nuclear fuels," have much
higher fission probabilities for thermal neutrons than for energetic
ones. In fact, the fission probability for U^{235} is more than 500
times greater with thermal neutrons than with neutrons having a
kinetic energy of several MeV. To enhance fission, the neutrons,
emitted with an average energy of 1.5 MeV, must be slowed down
—i.e., reduced in energy. This reduction is achieved by a **moderator,** some material of low Z showing a negligible absorption of
neutrons. Graphite, H_2O, and D_2O are good moderators. In
many reactors, the fuel elements and control rods are immersed in

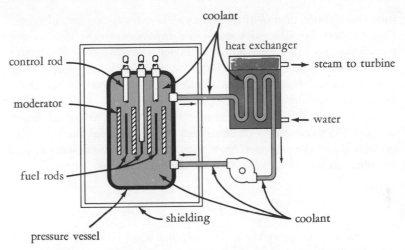

Figure 4–7 A nuclear reactor showing the use of a heat exchanger to provide steam for a turbine generating electricity.

a **reactor vessel** where a flow of H_2O or D_2O serves as both coolant and moderator. In order to reflect most of the neutrons that escape the reactor vessel back into it, thereby increasing neutron economy, the reactor vessel is surrounded by a **reflector.** Most commonly, this is beryllium (Fig. 4–7).

The reactor vessel must be surrounded by a thickness of material sufficient to absorb any neutrons and gamma rays emanating from the fission reaction in order to protect operating personnel. This shielding is sometimes water, more often concrete. Also required is a great deal of auxiliary equipment, the nature of which depends on the purpose of the reactor.

It is beyond the scope of this book to describe the wide variety of experimental and research reactors. Boiling-water reactors, pressurized-water reactors, gas-cooled reactors, breeder reactors, and swimming pool reactors are only a few of the types that have resulted from the imaginative minds of reactor physicists. In Britain, Russia, the United States, and several other countries, reactors are already being used to produce electricity that is fed into the electric grid of the country. The total amount of power thus produced is still quite small in comparison to the total power production by other means, and electricity produced from reactors is still more expensive than that from conventional sources such as fossil fuels. In some areas where fossil fuel power is expensive because of transportation costs, etc., nuclear power is very close to being competitive even now. However, on a broad scale, particularly in such oil-rich countries as the U.S. and the U.S.S.R., present estimates are that power from conventional sources will continue to be cheaper for another decade or more.

SUMMARY

Fission is possibly the most fascinating, the most complicated, and the most practically important nuclear reaction. Very heavy nuclei show spontaneous fission but nuclei as light as the lanthanide elements have been made to undergo fission by use of energetic projectiles. Approximately 200 MeV are liberated in fission, with 85 per cent of this energy appearing as the kinetic energies of the two large fission fragments. These two fragments vary in relative mass from equality (symmetric fission) to pronounced inequality (asymmetric fission). Since more than one neutron is emitted in the fission process, a chain reaction can be initiated. In a bomb, this chain reaction multiplies until the liberated fission energy blows the parent material apart. In a nuclear reactor, the chain is regulated within controllable limits by rapid removal of the energy and by the absorption of neutrons by control rods.

It is rather surprising that a process of such importance as fission—one that has been the object of so much study—is still in need of a satisfactory theoretical explanation. Such an explanation can only be advanced when a sufficient amount of experimental data has been obtained on all its aspects.

PROBLEMS

    1. Describe the liquid-drop model of the nucleus.
    2. Explain nuclear fission in terms of the liquid-drop model.
    3. Th^{232} does not undergo fission upon capture of thermal

neutrons. Show that the excitation energy of Th^{233} is less than the approximately 5.5-MeV activation energy required for fission.
$M_{Th}^{232} = 232.1000$; $M_{Th}^{233} = 233.1136$

4. Assume that the total kinetic energy of the fragments from the fission of U^{235} by thermal neutrons is 170 MeV; use the principle of conservation of momentum ($E_1M_1 = E_2M_2$) to calculate kinetic energies for $A = 80$, 90, 100, 110, 120, 130, 140, and 150. (Assume also that two neutrons are lost in fission.) Draw a curve, plotting kinetic energy vs. A.

Ans: For $A = 80$, $E = 112$ MeV

5. What is meant by a critical mass of uranium in a reactor?

6. Define these terms: fuel elements; control rods; moderator; reflector.

7. Assume that each fission can release neutrons to cause two further fissions in a chain reaction. Beginning with a single fission, how many MeV are released after ten generations if 200 MeV are released per fission? *Ans:* 2.05×10^5 *MeV*

8. Starting with $M_1V_1 = M_2V_2$, prove that $E_1/E_2 = M_2/M_1$.

V

Accelerators

I N 1919 Lord Rutherford fulfilled the age-old dream of the alchemists—he caused artificial transmutation of one element into another. When alpha particles from natural alpha-emitting nuclides such as Po^{214} were allowed to pass through nitrogen gas, energetic protons were observed. Rutherford correctly interpreted this observation to mean that the alpha particles were interacting with nitrogen nuclei to form oxygen and a proton; i.e.,

$$_7N^{14} + {_2}He^4 \rightarrow {_8}O^{17} + {_1}H^1$$

Since alpha particles from natural emitters have energies between 3 and 9 MeV, the nuclear coulomb barrier prevents their reaction with any but the lightest nuclei. Physicists began to search for a technique to obtain alpha particles of higher energies in order to extend the study of nuclear reactions to all the elements in the periodic table. By applying the same technique to hydrogen nuclei, proton-induced reactions could be studied also.

The principle to be used was obvious: hydrogen or helium atoms should be stripped of their electrons to form the positively charged nuclei. If the positively charged nuclei were allowed to pass through a tube with a voltage difference between the two ends of the tube, as shown schematically in Fig. 5–1, the nuclei would be

78

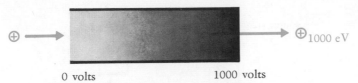

0 volts   1000 volts

Figure 5–1 A proton, in passing through an accelerator tube having a potential difference of 1000 volts between the ends, gains 1000 eV of kinetic energy.

accelerated in the tube and emerge at higher energy levels. If a proton were passed through such an "accelerator tube" having a potential difference of 1000 volts between the two ends, the proton would gain 1000 eV of energy. For helium nuclei passing through the same potential difference, the increase in energy would be 2000 eV since the alpha particle has a +2 charge. To cause a nuclear reaction, however, the projectile must have a minimum energy comparable to the height of the coulomb repulsive barrier; therefore the particles must gain millions of eV to be useful. The early accelerator physicists were faced with two major problems: first, techniques had to be developed for stripping the electrons from the atoms to form the positive ions; second, a means of supplying a very large potential difference across the accelerator tube had to be discovered.

The first problem was the easier to solve. If hydrogen gas is bombarded by energetic electrons, the gas will be ionized and protons produced. Fig. 5–2 shows a typical type of ion source. As the hydrogen flows into the region above the filament, the electrons being emitted by the filament are accelerated to a cathode and in their passage bombard the gas and ionize it. The extractor is at a negative potential in order to attract the positive ions out of the ion source and into the acceleration region. The extractor must be of open design to minimize collision with the positive ions.

The problem of developing a sufficient potential difference for the accelerator tube was more difficult to overcome. In 1922 J. D. Cockcroft and E. T. S. Walton, working in Rutherford's laboratory in Cambridge, England, caused the first nuclear reaction with artificially accelerated particles. Upon bombardment of a target

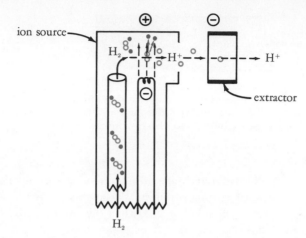

Figure 5–2 A schematic representation of an ion source producing protons by electron bombardment of hydrogen gas.

of lithium oxide with protons, alpha particles were produced by the reaction

$$_3Li^7 + {_1}H^1 \rightarrow {_2}He^4 + {_2}He^4$$

The protons were accelerated to several hundred thousand eV by a voltage-multiplier system using arrangements of condensers in cascade. Although the Cockcroft-Walton device has been developed to the point where particle energies of 3 MeV can be obtained with relatively high beam intensities, other acceleration techniques are more widely used today and will be discussed more fully.

5–1   Van de Graaff Generator

In 1931 R. J. Van de Graaff introduced an electrostatic generator that provided 1.5-MeV protons. This type of accelerator has been of great value to nuclear science since its invention, for it can provide particle beams of very precisely defined energy. In a modification known as the **Tandem Van de Graaff,** beams of 18-

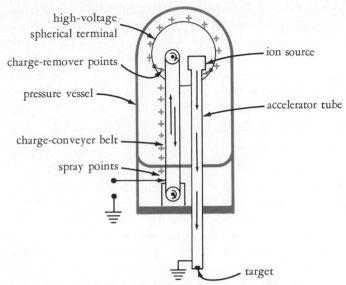

high-voltage
spherical terminal

charge-remover points

pressure vessel

charge-conveyer belt

spray points

ion source

accelerator tube

target

**Figure 5–3 Simplified diagram of a Van de Graaff elec-
trostatic generator, showing the transfer of positive
charge from the belt to the sphere. One end of the accelerating tube is connected to the sphere and, as a consequence, has the same electrostatic potential. The other
end of the tube is grounded (zero potential).**

MeV protons and of 27-MeV alphas have been produced. Electrons can also be accelerated in Van de Graaff generators.

Let us discuss the principle of the Van de Graaff generator by
considering the diagram of Fig. 5–3. A rapidly moving belt of
nonconducting material passes the sharp "spray points" where
electrons are transferred from the belt to the positively charged
spray points. The portion of the belt that has passed the spray
points now carries a positive charge up to another set of points;
these, by removing electrons from a hollow metal sphere, transfer
the positive charge to the sphere. It is a property of such a sphere
that the charge distributes itself evenly on the outer surface. The
belt continues to transfer charge and the potential of the sphere
rises until the rate of loss of charge by leakage across the insulators

equals the rate of addition from the belt. To minimize leakage loss, the sphere is enclosed in a pressure vessel containing a gas of high electron affinity such as SF_6. The accelerator tube is connected to the charged sphere, providing a potential difference through which the positive ions fall to gain energy before striking the target at the other end of the tube. The Van de Graaff design has advanced to the point where 9 million volts can be built up on the sphere, providing proton beams of 9 MeV.

5-2   Linear Accelerator

For several reasons it was desirable to extend the energy range of bombardments to many—even hundreds—of MeV. Unfortunately, the problems of insulator breakdown and leakage limited the voltages that could be obtained with Van de Graaff accelerators. Then E. O. Lawrence suggested that the acceleration could be achieved by having the particle receive a succession of small voltage "kicks" rather than a single large one. Lawrence showed that this principle could be used in two types of machine: the linear accelerator and the cyclotron. We shall discuss the linear accelerator first.

The diagram for a simple linear accelerator in Fig. 5-4 shows a series of hollow cylindrical electrodes in a straight line. All the even-numbered electrodes are connected together to terminal B; all the odd ones are similarly connected to terminal A. The two terminals are connected to a high-frequency oscillator, with the result that the polarity of the electrodes changes between positive and negative millions of times per sec. Consider a proton that

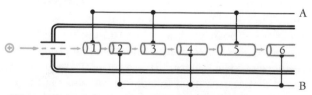

Figure 5-4   A linear accelerator for protons, showing the connection of alternate drift tubes.

emerges from electrode 1 as electrode 1 approaches its maximum positive potential and electrode 2 approaches its maximum negative potential. The proton will be accelerated across the gap between the electrodes, gaining energy corresponding to the potential difference between the two electrodes. Once inside the second electrode, the proton is in a region of uniform field; there it does not accelerate but remains constant in velocity and, therefore, in energy. (For this reason the electrodes are referred to as **drift tubes.**) The drift-tube length is such that during the time it takes for the proton to drift through it, the potential changes from negative to positive. When the proton emerges, electrode 2 is now positive and electrode 3 negative; thus the proton accelerates again. This process continues all the way down the length of the linear accelerator. The total energy gained by the proton is the sum of the energy increments gained at the drift-tube gaps. Since the velocity of the proton increases as it progresses down the accelerator whereas the oscillator frequency remains constant, it is necessary to make the drift tubes progressively longer, thus allowing the proton always to arrive at the exit of a tube in phase with the oscillation of the potential.

A linear accelerator of 40-ft length with 46 drift tubes was built at the University of California, Berkeley, after World War II. Protons were accelerated to 4 MeV in a Van de Graaff before injection into the linear accelerator where an additional 28 MeV was gained; thus each proton carried a total of 32 MeV at the exit of the accelerator. Linear accelerators to accelerate heavier ions have been built at Berkeley and at Yale University. Beams of boron, carbon, nitrogen, oxygen, and neon ions with energies as high as 200 MeV have been obtained, and both element 102 and element 103 were synthesized at Berkeley using the heavy-ion linear accelerator. At Stanford University an electron linear accelerator under construction is expected to produce electrons of 100 BeV (billion electron volts).

An effect that helps to produce beams of sufficient intensity for research in linear and other accelerators was first demonstrated by V. Veksler and E. McMillan independently but almost simultaneously. This principle of **phase stability** tends to keep the particles in phase with the oscillations of the potentials. In Fig. 5–5 the variation of potential

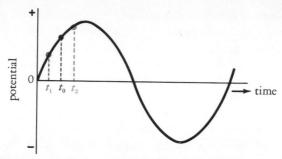

Figure 5–5   Variation of accelerator potential with time, demonstrating the principle of phase stability for particles arriving at the accelerating gap between t_1 and t_2.

with time is shown.   In operation, a particle in proper phase should arrive at the acceleration gap at time t_0.   If a particle has less energy, it takes longer to traverse the drift tube and arrives late at the gap—e.g., at time t_2.   Since the potential is now higher, it receives a greater acceleration and speeds up, thereby becoming more in phase.   If a particle is too energetic, it arrives too early at the gap (t_1) and receives a smaller acceleration, causing it also to be more in phase.   This bunching of the ions not only keeps the ions in phase for acceleration but also reduces the energy spread in the beam.

5–3   Cyclotron

In 1931, when Lawrence built the first small linear accelerator, microwave oscillators were still things of the future.   With the oscillators then available, the rate of polarity change of the drift tubes was so slow that the lengths of the individual drift tubes would have had to be excessively long to achieve acceleration energies sufficient to induce nuclear reactions.   Remember that the tube must be long enough to allow polarity reversal while the ions are drifting through it.   Lawrence had a brilliant idea of a way to overcome this difficulty.   He suggested accelerating the ions in the gap between the poles of a magnet.   A charged particle will be bent in a circular path in a magnetic field such that

$$r = \frac{mv}{He} \tag{5-1}$$

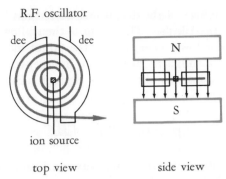

R.F. oscillator

dee   dee

N

S

ion source

top view   side view

Figure 5–6 Schematic diagrams of a cyclotron from the top and side. The vacuum tank, normally between the magnet faces and enclosing the "dees," is not shown.

where r is the radius of the path of the ion; m, v, and e are the mass, velocity, and charge of the ion, respectively; and H is the strength of the magnetic field. Therefore, instead of linear accelerators hundreds of feet long, Lawrence proposed circular accelerators, originally termed **magnetic-resonance accelerators** but later named **cyclotrons.**

The usual cyclotron consists of a rather large electromagnet with a vacuum chamber between the poles. In the vacuum chamber there is an ion source and two accelerating electrodes known as **dees.** These dees are flat, semicircular boxes connected to a radiofrequency oscillator (Fig. 5–6), and they behave just like the drift tubes in a linear accelerator. The ions leave the ion source and are accelerated to the negative dee. Under the influence of the magnetic field, they travel in a circular path inside the dee; here they are in a region of uniform electric field just as are ions inside a drift tube and, as in the latter, they remain at constant velocity. At the proper oscillator frequency, the polarity of the dees will reverse during passage of the ion through the dee. Thus, as it emerges from the original dee, the ion receives an acceleration across the gap between the two. This process of acceleration at the gaps and drifting in the dees continues, with the radius of the ion path increasing as the velocity increases. When the ion

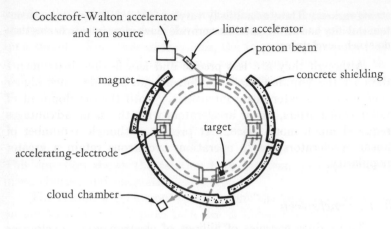

Figure 5-7   Diagram of the bevatron.

the energy to 10 MeV before injection into the bevatron proper where they are accelerated to a final energy of 6.2 BeV. The beam of approximately 10^{10} protons makes 4 million revolutions in going from 10 MeV to 6.2 BeV, a distance of 300,000 miles in a period of 1.8 sec. During this time, the magnetic field increases from 300 to 16,000 gauss and the RF frequency from 360 to 2500 kilocycles. Proton synchrotrons of 25- to 30-BeV energy beams are in operation at Brookhaven National Laboratory and at CERN in Switzerland. It is likely that 100-BeV machines may be built in the future.

SUMMARY

This has been only a brief discussion of the more common accelerators. Accelerator physics is a field of research populated by scientists of amazing ingenuity. An idea that appears to be wild fantasy when proposed often results in a practical and valuable accelerator only a few years later. We may continue to expect that improved accelerators at all energies will allow new areas of nuclear physics to be investigated.

For nuclear research requiring particles of relatively low (less than 20 MeV) but very precise energy, the Van de Graaff is of greatest value. Research on nuclear reactions induced by particle beams of 20 to several hundred MeV is conducted with the aid of cyclotrons and linear accelerators. Since the energy of the particles is not as precisely controlled as in a Van de Graaff, cyclotrons and linear accelerators cannot be used as readily for studies requiring precise energy definition. Proton synchrotrons extend the possible energy range into billions of eV.

PROBLEMS

1. Why is a particle only accelerated at the gap between the drift tubes in a linear accelerator?

2. Why is it necessary to constantly increase the length of the drift tubes in a linear accelerator?

3. Describe the principle of phase stability and its importance in accelerators.

4. If a cyclotron can accelerate alpha particles to 40 MeV, what maximum energy can be obtained for C^{6+} ions at the same values of r and H?   *Ans: 120 MeV*

5. Describe the principle of acceleration of particles in a cyclotron.

6. Cyclotrons that accelerate protons to energies of several hundred MeV have not used constant frequency. Why not?

7. Describe how a high-energy proton synchrotron operates.

8. How does an ion source produce positive ions for acceleration?

9. If a cyclotron of 40-inch radius produces proton beams of 20 MeV, at what radius must a target be placed internally to intercept the beam at a proton energy of 15 MeV?

Ans: 34.6-inches

VI

Nuclear Spectroscopy and Nuclear Reactions

I N CHAP. IV ON FISSION we discussed one of the areas of nuclear science in which nuclear chemists have been and continue to be quite active. Two other fields of particular activity for nuclear chemists are nuclear spectroscopy and nuclear reactions.

NUCLEAR SPECTROSCOPY

6–1 Decay Schemes

In Chap. II it was pointed out that the decay of U^{238}, in addition to alpha particles of 4.18 MeV (77 per cent) and 4.13 MeV (23 per cent), a 0.05-MeV gamma ray is emitted. Fig. 2–4 is a schematic representation of the probable relationship between the two alpha particles and the gamma ray. Such a diagram is known as the decay scheme for U^{238}. Verbally we describe the decay scheme in this fashion: All the alpha particles are emitted from U^{238} when the latter is in the ground (lowest energy) state. In 23 per cent of the decays, the U^{238} nucleus is transformed to a Th^{234}

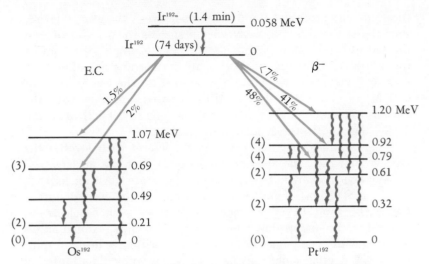

Figure 6–1 The decay scheme of Ir[192]. The number at the right of each level represents the energy difference (in MeV) between that level and the ground level. The number at the left is the nuclear spin.

nucleus that is in an excited rather than the ground state. The excited Th[234] nucleus decays to the ground state by emitting a gamma ray to carry off the excitation energy. From the two different alpha energy groups and from the gamma ray, we thus learn that Th[234] has an excited energy state (energy level) 0.05 MeV above the ground state.

The complexity of decay schemes varies greatly. A very simple decay scheme is that of Ar[39], a nuclide that decays directly to the ground state of K[39] by beta emission. The decay scheme of Ir[192] represents one of greater complexity. In an experimental study of this nuclide, it is possible to observe 17 gamma rays of different intensities. The decay scheme as depicted in Fig. 6–1 provides additional information on the nucleus. The numbers at the right of each level pattern are the energies of the various levels. The gamma rays observed in association with Ir[192] decay to Os[192] have energies of 1.07, 0.48, 0.38, 0.28, 0.21, and 0.20 MeV. Since these energies represent the differences between the energy levels, they can be fitted into a decay scheme such as the one shown, and the level energies can be calculated. For example, the gamma ray of 0.48-MeV energy must originate in the transition of an Os^{192} nucleus from the energy state of 0.69 MeV to the energy state of 0.21 MeV. Since the latter is still an excited, unstable state, the nucleus will immediately emit another gamma ray of 0.21 MeV and decay, thereby, to the ground state.

The number in parentheses at the left of each level is the nuclear spin (i.e., the angular momentum) that the nucleus possesses when it is in that particular energy state. All nuclei with even values of both Z and N have zero spin in the ground state— notice Os^{192} and Pt^{192}. Elementary particles such as electrons, protons, and neutrons have spins of $\frac{1}{2}$. Therefore, excited states of nuclei with even values of both Z and N will have integral spins —i.e., 1, 2, 3, etc.—since they have an even number of half-integral values. The particular pattern of spins is more difficult to predict, but a sequence of 0, 2, 4, 6 is often observed for heavy nuclei. Nuclei of even Z–odd N or of odd Z–even N have one nucleon beyond an even number and therefore the spins of their levels are not integral—e.g., the level pattern of Pu^{239} is $\frac{1}{2}$, $\frac{3}{2}$, $\frac{5}{2}$, $\frac{7}{2}$ for the first four levels. Since nuclei with odd values of both Z and N have an even total number of nucleons, integral spin values are again found for their levels; however, the spin at the ground-state level in such cases is not zero as it always is for nuclei with even values of Z and N.

It is difficult for gamma-ray emission to occur between levels of large spin difference. Notice in the decay scheme that the levels with spin values of 4 decay to levels of 4 and 2 but not to the spin 0 ground state. Instead, spin 4 levels decay to spin 2 levels and they, in turn, to the spin 0 level. This prohibition against large spin changes increases the number of gamma rays observed, since a nucleus may have to decay through several successive levels rather than directly to the ground state.

Although it is not possible in this book to discuss in detail the experimental techniques of nuclear spectroscopy, it will be apparent that fitting the observed beta- and gamma-ray energies into this nuclear jigsaw puzzle is a very fascinating process.

6-2   The Shell Model

There is a much more serious objective to determining decay schemes than the satisfaction of solving puzzles. The existence of energy levels demands a theory for the nucleus that can explain the energy and spin of these levels. In atomic physics, the energy levels of atoms are satisfactorily explained by the electron-shell theory first formulated by N. Bohr, who also suggested the liquid-drop model for the nucleus. Although the liquid-drop model explains many of the features of fission, it is of little value in predicting nuclear energy levels that are in agreement with those observed in decay schemes. Based on the observation of periodic behavior in nuclear binding energies, magnetic properties, and other characteristics, a nuclear shell theory has been formulated that is much more successful in level scheme predictions. The chemical inertness of the rare gases is easily explained by the stability of the closed electron shells for systems having 2, 10, 18, 36, 54, and 86 electrons. Similarly, relative nuclear inertness with respect to the capture of neutrons is observed for nuclei that have 2, 8, 20, 28, 50, 82, or 126 neutrons. This indicates, then, that closed nucleon shells are present in nuclei with 2, 8, 20, 28, 50, 82, or 126 neutrons or protons. These numbers are known as the nuclear "magic numbers." Two important differences exist between the electron shell model and the nucleon shell model. First, the protons and the neutrons in the nucleus exist in separate shells, with the result that there are proton-magic-number nuclei and neutron-magic-number nuclei. Thus, nuclei with either $Z = 50$ (e.g., Sn) or $N = 50$ (e.g., Sr^{88} and Zr^{90}) are magic (i.e., comparatively stable), whereas nuclei with $N + Z = 50$ are not magic unless either N or Z happens to have a value of 20 or 28 (e.g., Ti^{50}). Lead-212, with $N = 126$ and $Z = 82$, is doubly magic and is an unusually stable nuclide. Second, whereas the electrons are relatively far from the nucleus and from each other in an atom, the nucleons are packed closely in a nucleus. It is possible for the atomic scientist to treat together all the other electrons and the nucleus as a single body interacting with any one electron; his problem, then, is simply that of two bodies interacting by coulomb force action. The proximity of nucleons to one another and the presence of nuclear forces complicate immensely the problem of the nuclear scientist, for they demand a multibody, multiforce treatment. As a result of this greater complexity, we cannot expect the nuclear shell model to be as successful as the atomic shell model in predicting experimental results.

The level pattern derived for the nuclear shell model is shown in Table 6–1. It is most successful in predicting level schemes

Table 6–1
The Nuclear Level Pattern of the Shell Model

Level-designation	Neutron or proton capacity	Neutrons or protons, total number
$1s_{1/2}$	2	2
$2p_{3/2}$	4	
$2p_{1/2}$	2	8
$3d_{5/2}$	6	
$3d_{3/2}$	4	
$2s_{1/2}$	2	20
$4f_{7/2}$	8	28
$4f_{5/2}$	6	
$3p_{3/2}$	4	
$3p_{1/2}$	2	
$5g_{9/2}$	10	50
$5g_{7/2}$	8	
$4d_{5/2}$	6	
$4d_{3/2}$	4	
$3s_{1/2}$	2	
$6h_{11/2}$	12	82
$6h_{9/2}$	10	
$5f_{7/2}$	8	
$5f_{5/2}$	6	
$4p_{3/2}$	4	
$4p_{1/2}$	2	
$7i_{13/2}$	14	126

and spins for nuclei that have an N or a Z value close to one of the magic numbers. For example, In^{113} has $Z = 49$ and $N = 64$. The neutron number being even, the neutrons will produce no net spin. The odd proton, the 49th, is expected from the shell model to be in a $5g_{9/2}$ state. This predicts, then, a nuclear spin of $\frac{9}{2}$ for In^{113}, exactly the one observed. Similarly, for Sn^{125} the 51st proton is expected to be in a $5g_{7/2}$ state, predicting a nuclear spin of $\frac{7}{2}$, and this again agrees with observation.

In Sec. 2–1, it was stated that nuclear stability was decreased by increasing the n/p value. We can understand this now as resulting from the necessity of adding the extra neutrons to fill shells at higher energy levels. Instability accompanying too low n/p values is explained on the basis of the necessity of filling higher energy levels of protons.

6–3   The Collective Model

The shell model is progressively less successful in predicting energy levels for nuclei as the N and Z values depart from the magic numbers. Consequently, the more nucleons that nuclei are lacking for or have in excess of closed shells, the less valid is the level scheme of Table 6–1. A. Bohr, the son of N. Bohr, and B. Mottleson have proposed a theory that is much more successful in these regions between closed shells. Their theory utilizes what is known as the **collective model** of the nucleus.

The basic assumption of the liquid-drop model is that all the nucleons in the nucleus interact strongly, so the energy levels of the nucleus are due to the total collective action of the nucleons. The nucleus rotates and vibrates as a whole in different energy states, giving rise to rotational and vibrational energy levels. The basic assumption of the shell model is that an unpaired nucleon exists in a potential-well set up by all the other paired nucleons. Another way of saying this is that all the paired nucleons form a sphere and the energy levels resulting from interaction between this spherical core and the unpaired nucleon are the energy levels for the nucleus. A name used for the shell model that aptly describes this feature is the **single-particle model,** the energy levels being due to the behavior of the one or two unpaired nucleons.

In the collective model, Bohr and Mottleson have combined the liquid-drop and the single-particle models. Nuclei near magic numbers for either protons or neutrons will still have a spherical core, and their energy levels are described satisfactorily by the shell model. However, in the mass regions between closed-shell configurations, the core has a number of nucleons beyond the spherical closed shell. These nucleons interact as in a liquid drop, with the closed-shell sphere to create rotational and vibrational energy states. For nuclei with an unpaired nucleon, the odd nucleon still moves in the potential well created by the paired nucleons but the paired nucleon core may or may not be spherical. If it is almost spherical (close to closed-shell mass regions and hence requiring large energies for deformation), the low energy levels are the single-particle levels. If the core is nonspherical (having a large number of nucleons beyond a closed shell and hence deformable by relatively little energy), there may be vibrational and rotational energy levels lower than the single-particle levels. Nuclei in the lanthanide element and actinide element regions show nonspherical shapes. The level-pattern of $\frac{1}{2}$, $\frac{3}{2}$, $\frac{5}{2}$, $\frac{7}{2}$ for the first four levels of Pu^{239} is interpreted as resulting from four different rotation states of lower energy than the lowest-energy single-particle excited state. In general, there are two nuclear shapes that can cause these low-energy rotations and vibrations, the prolate spheroid (football-shaped) and the oblate spheroid (door-knob-shaped). This collective model has enjoyed considerable success in correlating the observed level patterns of a great many nuclei.

NUCLEAR REACTIONS

6-4   The Compound-Nucleus Theory

As the excitation energy of an excited nucleus increases, the energy levels get closer together. Eventually, a **continuum** is reached where the density of nuclear levels is so great that it is no longer possible to identify individual levels. This is also the case for electronic energy levels of atoms. When the excited nucleus emits a proton or neutron while in this high-energy condition, the resultant nucleus is frequently still sufficiently energetic that it too is in the continuum region.

N. Bohr has offered a mechanism to explain nuclear reactions with excitation energies beyond the range of discrete levels. In this mechanism, one based on his liquid-drop model, a bombarding particle strikes and is absorbed by the nucleus. The kinetic energy of the bombarding particle and the binding energy released by its absorption serve to excite the new **compound nucleus.** The whole compound nucleus becomes uniformly excited in a manner somewhat analogous to the warming of a small glass of water upon addition of a tablespoon of boiling water. As the nucleons bounce about in the nucleus, they increase and decrease in their individual kinetic energies, their behavior resembling that of molecules in a gas or liquid. With increase of the time interval from initial absorption, there is a corresponding increase in probability that at least one nucleon will gain kinetic energy in excess of its binding energy. That nucleon is then evaporated (i.e., leaves the nucleus) in the same sense that molecules are evaporated from liquid surfaces (Fig. 6–2).

The evaporation of the nucleon decreases the excitation energy of the nucleus by an amount corresponding to the binding energy plus the kinetic energy of the released nucleon. The evaporation process continues until the residual excitation energy is less than the binding energy of a nucleon. This remaining excita-

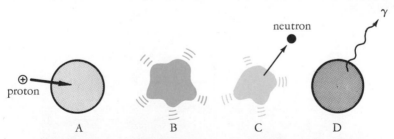

Figure 6–2   A simple representation of the formation of an excited compound nucleus B and its subsequent de-excitation by neutron evaporation C and gamma-ray emission D.

tion energy is removed from the nucleus by emission of gamma rays.

Let us assume that the Os^{188} compound nucleus has been formed with a total excitation energy of 20 MeV. If the average binding energy is 6 MeV and if each neutron removes 3 MeV, evaporation of a neutron de-excites the nucleus by 9 MeV. Therefore, evaporation of two neutrons will leave the residual Os^{186} nucleus with an excitation energy of only 2 MeV. Since this is below the binding energy of a neutron, further evaporation is not possible and gamma-ray emission removes the final 2 MeV. If the Os^{188} compound nucleus was formed by alpha bombardment of W^{184}, the reaction is represented

$$W^{184}(\alpha,2n)Os^{186}$$

6-5   Time of Compound-Nucleus Existence

One of the important assumptions of the Bohr compound-nucleus theory is that the time it takes for accidental accumulation on one nucleon of enough energy to cause evaporation is long by nuclear standards. This time is of the order of 10^{-14} sec compared to a time of 10^{-21} sec required for a nucleon to cross the nuclear diameter once. Since the time is so long and there are so many internucleon collisions, the nucleus retains no pattern ("no memory") of its mode of formation, and the mode of decay is therefore independent of the mode of formation. If, for example, the compound nucleus Os^{188} is formed in several different ways, as shown in Fig. 6–3, the mode of decay is primarily a function of the excita-

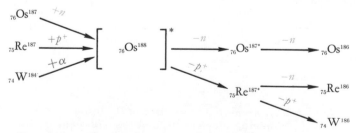

Figure 6–3   Nuclear reactions involved in the formation and subsequent decay of the Os^{188} compound nucleus.

tion energy of the Os^{188} and not of what reactions ($Re^{187} + p$, $W^{184} + \alpha$, etc.) were the formation reactions.

Possible decay paths involving the emission of two nucleons are shown for the Os^{188} system in Fig. 6–3. In general, neutron emission is favored over proton emission for two reasons. First, since there are more neutrons than protons ($n/p \approx 1.46$), a neutron is likely to accumulate the necessary evaporation energy before a proton does. Second, a neutron can depart from the nucleus with a low kinetic energy—the average neutron kinetic energy is 2 to 3 MeV. Therefore neutrons need to accumulate only a little more than their binding energy. On the other hand, evaporating protons must penetrate the coulomb barrier (see Chap. I), so they often need 5 to 10 MeV beyond their binding energy. It takes longer for this amount (≈ 12 MeV vs. ≈ 8 MeV for neutrons) to be concentrated on a nucleon. It is to be expected, then, that Os^{186} will be produced in higher yield than will Re^{186}, and Re^{186} in higher yield than W^{186}. It must be understood at this point that such a simple picture ignores a large number of complicating effects that can in particular cases reverse these yield orders. Nevertheless, despite its simplicity, the compound-nucleus theory has been of great value in explaining many aspects of medium-energy nuclear reactions (10 to 50 MeV bombarding energy).

6–6   Cross Sections

The probability for a nuclear reaction is expressed in terms of the cross section for the reaction. The geometric cross section that the nucleus presents to a beam of particles is πr^2. If we use 6×10^{-13} cm as an average value for nuclear radii, the value of πr^2 becomes $3.14 \times (6 \times 10^{-13})^2 \approx 10^{-24}$ cm². If the beam of particles is composed of neutrons, this geometric cross section should be a good measure of the reaction probability since there are no coulomb-interaction effects. The unit of reaction-probability cross section is the barn, with

$$1 \text{ barn} = 10^{-24} \text{ cm}^2$$

Experimentally, the cross section for neutron capture is often close to 1 barn. For very low-energy neutrons, some nuclei show very large cross sections—as high as 10^5 barns. Such values are due to capture where the compound nucleus is excited exactly to one of its discrete energy levels. This does not mean that the nucleus is larger than its calculated geometric cross section but that the interaction probability is very great in these cases—greater than our simple considerations in the calculation of πr^2 would indicate.

In order that their probabilities of capture be high, charged particles must have energies close to or greater than the height of the repulsive coulomb barrier. Since such energies may be equivalent to several times the average nucleon binding energies, the removal of the excitation energy may proceed in several steps and by more than one evaporation sequence. The sum of the cross sections for the individual reactions at any energy is equal to the cross section for formation of the compound nucleus. For the reaction

$$ A + a \xrightarrow{\sigma_f} [B]^* \underset{\sigma_d}{\overset{\sigma_c}{\rightarrow}} C + c $$
$$ \sigma_d \searrow D + d $$

σ_f, the formation cross section for the compound nucleus, equals $\sigma_c + \sigma_d$, the sum of the individual production cross sections for C and D. In Figs. 6–5 and 6–6, the cross sections for individual reactions are plotted as a function of bombarding energies. Such curves (cross section vs. bombardment energy) are known as **excitation functions.**

6–7   Direct Interaction

The compound-nucleus theory considers that the bombarding particle interacts with the nucleus as a whole. The nucleus is excited uniformly and evaporation of low-energy nucleons follows. As the kinetic energy of the bombarding particle increases, this model fails to explain some of the observed phenomena. One such observation is the occurrence of high-energy neutrons and protons in the emitted particles; another is a cross section much larger than expected for reactions such as $A(p, pn)C$ at energies where six or seven nucleons should have to be evaporated in order to de-excite the nucleus.

R. Serber has suggested the mechanism that satisfactorily accounts for most features of nuclear reactions at bombardment energies (for protons, deuterons, and alphas) above 50 MeV.

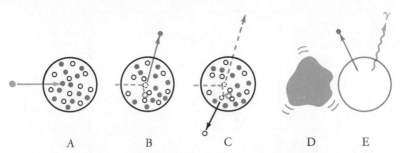

Figure 6–4 A simple representation of a high-energy reaction in which a neutron (B) and a proton (C) are directly knocked out before formation of the compound nucleus D and subsequent de-excitation by evaporation and gamma-ray emission E.

According to his theory, a high-energy reaction is considered to occur in two stages (Fig. 6–4). During the first stage, the incoming particle undergoes direct collision with individual nucleons. In these collisions, the struck nucleon often receives energy much in excess of its binding energy. Consequently, after each collision, both the initial bombarding particle and the struck nucleon have some probability of escaping the nucleus. If both particles escape, the nucleus is usually left with only a small amount of excitation energy. Thus is explained the appearance of high-energy protons and neutrons.

If either one or both of the original pair remain in the nucleus, they will collide with other nucleons with the same possibility of escape. During this initial stage, known as the **knock-on cascade** process, the total number of direct collisions may be one or many. After a period lasting about 10^{-19} sec, some of the struck nucleons have left the nucleus and the remainder have become so degraded in energy that the residual excitation energy is uniformly distributed. The reaction then enters its second and slower stage, during which the residual excitation energy is lost by nucleon evaporation. This stage resembles the compound-nucleus process very closely.

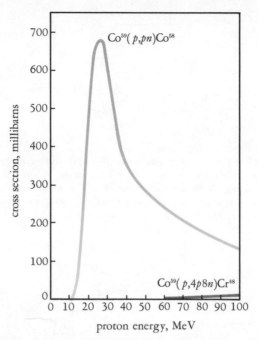

Figure 6–5   Excitation functions for the formation of Co^{58} and Cr^{48} from proton bombardment of Co^{59}.

The excitation functions for the reactions Co$^{59}(p,pn)$Co^{58} and Co$^{59}(p,4p8n)$Cr^{48} are shown in Fig. 6–5.   The curve for the (p,pn) reaction resembles the shape of those for compound-nucleus reactions at energies between 12 and 35 MeV.   The long tail for the cross section at energies above 40 MeV is evidence for a process whereby the bombarding proton knocks a neutron out of the nucleus, then itself leaves.   This process should be relatively independent of the proton energy, as is shown by the slow decrease in cross section with energy.   The slow rise in cross section for the $(p,4p8n)$ reaction as the energy increases indicates that this is a knock-on process followed by evaporation.

6-8   Energetics of Nuclear Reactions

In a nuclear reaction as in nuclear decay, mass and energy must be conserved. Consider the reactions

$$\text{Th}^{232} (\alpha, n) \text{ U}^{235} \qquad (a)$$

$$\text{Th}^{232} (\alpha, 2n) \text{ U}^{234} \qquad (b)$$

$$\text{Th}^{232} (\alpha, 3n) \text{ U}^{233} \qquad (c)$$

$$\text{Th}^{232} (\alpha, 4n) \text{ U}^{232} \qquad (d)$$

Given the following masses

$$_0n^1 = 1.0090 \text{ amu} \qquad \text{U}^{232} = 232.1095 \text{ amu}$$

$$_2\text{He}^4 = 4.0038 \qquad \text{U}^{233} = 233.1121$$

$$\text{Th}^{232} = 232.1105 \qquad \text{U}^{234} = 234.1139$$

$$\text{U}^{235} = 235.1172$$

it is possible to calculate the energies involved by the method in Chap. I. Let us use reaction (a)—the (α, n) reaction—as an example.

$$\text{Th}^{232} + \text{He}^4 \rightarrow \text{U}^{235} + n + Q$$

$$Q_1 = 931 \left[(M_{\text{Th}} + M_{\text{He}}) - (M_{\text{U}} + M_n) \right]$$

$$= 931 (236.1143 - 236.1262) = 931 (-0.0119)$$

Therefore

$$Q_1 = -11.1 \text{ MeV}$$

The negative sign shows that this is an endothermic reaction so that at least 11.1 MeV of energy must be supplied to the system. This is the threshold energy below which the $\text{Th}^{232} (\alpha,n) \text{U}^{235}$ reaction thermodynamically cannot occur.

Similar calculations yield the following threshold values for the other reactions:

$$\text{Th}^{232}(\alpha,2n)\text{U}^{234} \qquad Q_2 = -16.4 \text{ MeV} \qquad (b)$$

$$\text{Th}^{232}(\alpha,3n)\text{U}^{233} \qquad Q_3 = -23.2 \text{ MeV} \qquad (c)$$

$$\text{Th}^{232}(\alpha,4n)\text{U}^{232} \qquad Q_4 = -29.0 \text{ MeV} \qquad (d)$$

The question that naturally arises is whether these reactions can in fact proceed when these threshold energies are provided. The Th^{232}

nucleus is essentially at rest, so the incoming alpha particle must bring in the reaction energy as kinetic energy. We are all familiar with the fact that some translational kinetic energy is imparted to a heavy ball when a fast-moving lighter one strikes it; this transfer is necessary to conserve linear momentum in the system. When the alpha particle strikes the Th^{232} to form the compound nucleus U^{236}, the compound nucleus uses a fraction of the kinetic energy of the alpha particle as simple translational energy. Consequently, the kinetic energy of the alpha particle must be greater than 11.1 MeV by the amount of this translational energy if the particle is to provide the nucleus with the 11.1 MeV needed for the (α,n) reaction.

In Chap. II we discussed conservation of momentum and from that discussion we know that the amount of extra alpha-particle kinetic energy necessary to conserve momentum is 4/236 of the total kinetic energy. Therefore the total kinetic energy necessary to provide 11.1 MeV of nuclear energy is

$$(\text{K.E.})_1 = 11.1 \times \frac{236}{232} = 11.3 \text{ MeV} \qquad (a')$$

The other reactions similarly require the following kinetic energies from the alpha particles:

$$(\text{K.E.})_2 = 16.4 \times \frac{236}{232} = 16.7 \text{ MeV} \qquad (b')$$

$$(\text{K.E.})_3 = 23.2 \times \frac{236}{232} = 23.6 \text{ MeV} \qquad (c')$$

$$(\text{K.E.})_4 = 29.0 \times \frac{236}{232} = 29.5 \text{ MeV} \qquad (d')$$

In all the preceding discussion, we have ignored any effects resulting from repulsion by the coulomb barrier. Unless the alpha particle can pass through or over the coulomb barrier to reach the surface of the Th^{232} nucleus, it cannot be absorbed even if its kinetic energy can satisfy the thermodynamic requirements. For Th^{232} the coulomb barrier to the approach of alpha particles is almost 24 MeV. Th^{232} emits alpha particles of 4.00 MeV with a half-life of 1.4×10^{10} years despite this 24-MeV barrier. However, we saw in Chap. II that this was due to the tremendously large number of times that the alpha particle hits the barrier. A bombarding alpha particle presents itself to the barrier only once, and the probability of penetration by a 4.00-MeV alpha particle is only about one in 10^{38}. As a result, the alpha particles must have kinetic energies closely corre-

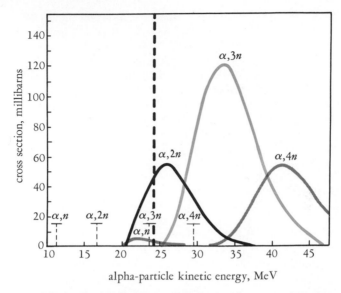

Figure 6–6   Excitation functions for nuclear reactions induced by alpha-particle bombardment of Th²³². The short dashed lines indicate the calculated threshold energies for the reactions; the heavy broken line indicates the calculated coulomb barrier (classical).

sponding to the coulomb-barrier height in order to penetrate to the Th²³² nucleus for reaction. Cross sections for the (α,n) and $(\alpha,2n)$ reactions are therefore quite small at energies below 20 MeV, even though the reactions are energetically possible.

In Fig. 6–6, the experimental excitation curves for the reactions that we have been discussing are shown. Notice that the (α,n) reaction curve only reaches 6 millibarns (1 millibarn = 10^{-3} barns). An alpha particle with sufficient kinetic energy to pass over the coulomb barrier imparts considerable excitation energy to the nucleus—enough, in fact, as the curves show, to allow evaporation of two neutrons more often than of just one. The existence of the coulomb barrier serves to reduce the (α,n) reaction cross section very considerably. This same explanation serves to account for the greater magnitude of the $(\alpha,3n)$ reaction cross section relative to that of the $(\alpha,2n)$ at their maximum energies. It must be pointed out, also, that in this system of $Th^{232} + He^4$, 80 to 90 per cent of the compound nuclei undergo fission rather than de-excitation by neutron evaporation. Fission can occur not only for the U^{236} compound nucleus but also for the residual nucleus after each neutron evaporation until the excitation energy is below 6 to 7 MeV. Let us assume that for each nucleus in the evaporation chain, the probability of fission and of neutron evaporation is equal (i.e., 50 per cent each). Then for Th^{232} $(\alpha, 4n)U^{232}$ to occur, the probability is $(0.5)^4$ or 0.06. Only 6 per cent of the nuclei survive fission in the four-step chain. Consequently, most of the 1- to 2-barn formation cross section goes to fission and only a small percentage of the total cross section appears as complete de-excitation by neutron evaporation.

6–9   Production of Nuclides

A wide variety of types of nuclear reaction have been used to produce new nuclides. To illustrate this variety, we shall consider the production of the new transuranium elements. Table 6–2 lists a number of charged-particle reactions that have been of interest in the study of these actinide elements.

In reactions with He^4, C^{12}, O^{16}, etc., equal numbers of protons and neutrons are added to the nucleus. Since neutrons are usually evaporated in preference to protons, the final nucleus is often neutron-deficient and has an n/p ratio below stability. These low n/p values cause many of the products of charged-particle-induced

Table 6–2

$$_{92}U^{238} + {}_1H^2 \rightarrow {}_{93}Np^{238} + n$$
$$_{92}U^{238} + {}_2He^4 \rightarrow {}_{94}Pu^{239} + 3n$$
$$_{94}Pu^{239} + {}_2He^4 \rightarrow {}_{95}Am^{240} + p2n$$
$$_{94}Pu^{239} + {}_2He^4 \rightarrow {}_{96}Cm^{242} + n$$
$$_{96}Cm^{244} + {}_2He^4 \rightarrow {}_{97}Bk^{245} + p2n$$
$$_{92}U^{238} + {}_6C^{12} \rightarrow {}_{98}Cf^{246} + 4n$$
$$_{92}U^{238} + {}_7N^{14} \rightarrow {}_{99}Es^{247} + 5n$$
$$_{92}U^{238} + {}_8O^{16} \rightarrow {}_{100}Fm^{249} + 5n$$
$$_{99}Es^{253} + {}_2He^4 \rightarrow {}_{101}Md^{256} + n$$
$$_{96}Cm^{246} + {}_6C^{13} \rightarrow {}_{102}No^{254} + 5n$$
$$_{98}Cf^{252} + {}_5B^{10} \rightarrow {}_{103}Lw^{257} + 5n$$

nuclear reactions to be unstable to positron emission or electron capture.

Another useful nuclear reaction is neutron capture. In Chap. IV we discussed thermal neutron capture followed by fission. In nonfissionable elements, and to some extent even in the fissionable elements, the nucleus de-excites following thermal neutron capture by gamma emission only. Thermal neutron capture provides an excitation energy only very slightly greater than the neutron binding energy, and it would be necessary that all the excitation energy accidentally accumulate on one nucleon for evaporation. Since this accumulation has such a low probability of occurrence, gamma-ray emission occurs in preference to neutron emission. If the neutrons have several MeV or more of kinetic energy, one or more nucleons may be evaporated from the excited nucleus prior to gamma emission. Nuclear reactors are sources of large numbers of neutrons, and neutron-capture reactions are usually carried out in reactors. Since neutrons are being added to the nucleus, the latter becomes more neutron-rich (high n/p value) and will most probably undergo negatron (β^-) decay if it is beta-unstable. The over-all series of changes that often occurs can be represented in this fashion:

$$_Z M^A (n,\gamma) {}_Z M^{A+1} \xrightarrow{\beta^-} {}_{Z+1} N^{A+1}$$

The actinide elements have been produced by long-term irradiation in reactors. Beginning with several grams of Pu^{239}, 2 years of continuous irradiation will yield a mixture containing $_{100}Fm^{254}$ as well as all the elements between $Z = 94$ and $Z = 100$. The over-all process for the production of Fm^{254} is shown in Fig. 6-7. Most of the Pu^{239} is converted to fission products, with the result that very high levels of radiation become associated with the irradiated sample. To protect the chemist, separation and purification of the actinide elements produced in such a sample must be carried out in thick, lead caves by remote-control operation. Despite the problems connected with such operation, reactor irradiation is the only method practical for production of relatively large amounts of these elements. Gram amounts of americium and curium, milligram amounts of berkelium and californium, and microgram amounts of einsteinium are already available or soon

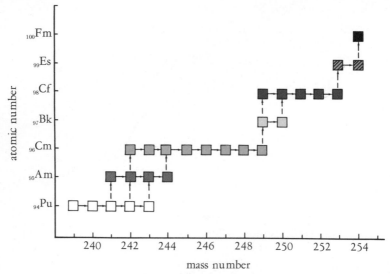

Figure 6–7   Reaction and decay sequence for production
of the actinide elements by irradiation of Pu^{239} in a nuclear
reactor.

will be as a result of such neutron irradiations.   Unfortunately,
problems of small cross sections and short half-lives prevent production of elements above $Z = 100$ by this technique at present.

The initial discovery of elements 99, einsteinium, and 100, fermium,
followed their production by neutron-induced reaction, not in a reactor
but in the explosion of a hydrogen bomb.   In this explosion, one that
occurred in November of 1952 under the code name "Mike," a rather
large amount of U^{238} was used.   As a result extremely large numbers of
neutrons were released, and these bombarded the uranium causing most
of it to undergo fission.   In the debris of the explosion, a few atoms of
Cf^{254}, Es^{255}, and Fm^{255} were discovered along with heavy isotopes of Pu,
Am, Cm, and Bk.   Presumably, a very few of the U^{238} nuclei captured as
many as 17 neutrons in a very short time.   Since the resultant nuclides
had quite large n/p values, they experienced rapid, successive beta decays
until nuclides were reached with half-lives that were long compared to the
time it took to separate the actinides.

6-10   Thermonuclear Fusion Reactions

Before concluding the topic of nuclear reactions, a brief discussion of fusion reactions is pertinent since successful utilization of the power released in fusion reactions would be of almost unimaginable benefit to civilization. The energy available from fusion of the deuterium in sea water is a thousand million times greater than all the combustion energy in all the fossil fuels (coal, petroleum, etc.) in the world. The world would have its energy requirements satisfied for millions of years. For the present, the energy of fusion can be released on earth only in the uncontrollable explosion of a hydrogen bomb, a situation that excludes its use as an energy source for other than explosive purposes.

Although the binding-energy curve (Fig. 1–3) indicates that fusion reactions are exothermic up to $A \approx 60$, the largest energy release occurs with the lightest nuclides. Two important reactions are

$$_1\text{H}^2 + {}_1\text{H}^2 \rightarrow {}_2\text{He}^3 + {}_0n^1$$

$$_1\text{H}^2 + {}_1\text{H}^3 \rightarrow {}_2\text{He}^4 + {}_0n^1$$

To make possible these reactions, the coulombic repulsion must be overcome, a collision energy of 0.02 MeV being required. The deuterium and tritium atoms must be at a temperature greater than 200 million degrees to have kinetic energies of this magnitude. Of course, such reactions can easily be achieved by Van de Graaff accelerators, etc., but not in numbers sufficient to produce energy equal to the power requirements of the accelerators themselves. Consequently, successful power production cannot be obtained with accelerators. Atoms with kinetic energies of 0.02 MeV exist only as gases. In fact, these atoms are so energetic that their electrons have escaped, and the hot gas really consists of ions and electrons. Such a gas is known as a **plasma.** The plasma cannot be allowed to strike a solid wall since heat transfer would result in the rapid cooling of the plasma below the reaction temperature and the melting of the wall. The answer seems to lie in using matterless walls of magnetic fields. These magnetic fields can keep the plasma concentrated in the same way that the bevatron magnets hold the proton beam in its circular path; they can serve to prevent collision with the walls and to hold the plasma in the reaction volume while its density is being increased sufficiently to achieve a significant amount of fusion. Research at the University of California, Princeton, Los Alamos, and Oak Ridge in the United States, as well as in England and in Russia, has produced promising results, but present indications are that economic fusion power will require several more decades of research.

In hydrogen bombs, the temperatures necessary to initiate the fusion reaction are obtained by using small atomic (fission) bombs. The release of fission energy by the atomic bomb trigger heats the surrounding fusionable material sufficiently to initiate the fusion reaction, thereby releasing much greater amounts of energy. Since in a very rapid time this energy causes vaporization of the bomb material, only a small fraction of the total material actually undergoes fusion. If a jacket of U^{238} is placed around the outside of the fusionable material, two advantages are realized. First, uranium is so heavy and has such a high boiling point that it can cause the thermonuclear fusion to continue slightly longer, thus achieving a higher yield of energy per unit weight of fusion material. Second, fission of the uranium by neutrons from the fusion reaction can add to the total energy released in the explosion.

The products from fusion reactions are either stable or have very short half-lives. However, the fission products formed by the A-bomb trigger and by the uranium jacket (if there is one) are more of a radiation hazard. When the debris of the H-bomb explosion settles to earth, fission-product nuclides such as Sr^{90}, I^{131}, and Cs^{137} do constitute a danger to mankind. Since this "fallout" occurs over a period of time extending to years and over a large portion of the earth, Sr^{90} and Cs^{137} continue to accumulate in our environment as bomb testing continues anywhere in the world. Although scientists are still divided on the rate of accumulation of the radioactivity and the consequent danger to us and to future generations, there is agreement that fallout radiation is causing some damage (e.g., an increase in the incidence of leukemia). A much longer period of observation is necessary before sufficient scientific data can be accumulated to assess fully the danger of radioactivity to humans.

SUMMARY

The success of the shell model of the atom caused physicists to formulate an analogous theory for the nucleus. Near magic-number nuclei in particular, the shell model of the nucleus has proved to be a useful concept. For certain reactions, of which fission is a good example, the nuclear model that more satisfactorily explains many observations is based on an analogy with the dynamics of a liquid drop. In the shell model, the energy levels of the nucleus are described by the behavior of an individual nucleon moving in a potential generated by all the other nucleons. In the liquid-drop model, the energy levels are described by the behavior of the nucleus acting as a unit, vibrating and rotating like a drop of incompressible liquid.

These two models have been combined in the collective nuclear model. In this model both the single-particle energy levels and the vibrational-rotational energy levels are possible. For nuclei near magic numbers, the single-particle levels are lower in energy, whereas for nuclei between magic numbers, the vibrational and rotational levels are lower in energy.

In nuclear reactions, the concept of the formation of an excited compound nucleus has been quite useful. The nucleus is de-excited by evaporation of nucleons. The mode of decay is determined by the energy and angular momentum of the compound nucleus rather than by the mode of formation of the compound nucleus. At higher energies, the incoming projectile may cause direct "knock-out" of several nucleons prior to the slower nucleon-evaporation step in the de-excitation.

PROBLEMS

1. In the decay of Cs^{137}, beta groups having endpoint energies of 0.51 and 1.17 MeV are observed along with gamma rays of 0.66 MeV. Draw a possible decay scheme for Cs^{137}.

2. In the decay of Th^{226}, alpha particles having energies of 6.33, 6.22, 6.10, and 6.03 MeV are observed. In addition, gamma rays of 0.11, 0.13, 0.20, and 0.24 MeV have been measured. Suggest a decay scheme compatible with this data.

3. What are nuclear magic numbers? Give five nuclides that are magic-number nuclides.

4. Describe the compound-nucleus model for nuclear reactions.

5. Calculate the energy thresholds for the following reactions:

(a) $U^{238} + C^{12} \rightarrow Cf^{247} + 3n$

(b) $U^{238} + C^{12} \rightarrow Cf^{246} + 4n$

where $M_{U^{238}} = 238.1245$; $M_{Cf^{246}} = 246.1451$; $M_{Cf^{247}} = 247.1476$; $M_{C^{12}} = 12.0038$ *Ans: $Cf^{247} = 43.2 \ MeV$*

6. Calculate the coulomb barrier for $U^{238} + C^{12}$, using $R_0 = 1.4 \times 10^{-13}$ cm.   *Ans: 66.8 MeV*

7. Calculate the energy released in the following thermonuclear reactions:

(a) $_1H^2 + _1H^2 \rightarrow _2He^3 + n$

(b) $_1H^2 + _1H^3 \rightarrow _2He^4 + n$

where $M_{H^2} = 2.0147$; $M_{H^3} = 3.0170$; $M_{He^3} = 3.0170$; $M_{He^4} = 4.0038$ *Ans: $He^3 = 3.2 \ MeV$*

8. Draw the reaction and decay sequence for the production of Cm^{246} from Am^{241} by neutron irradiation.

VII

Uses of Radioisotopes

UP TO THIS POINT, our discussion has been concerned with nuclear science. Nuclear theory and radioactive instability have been considered, along with the most important technical tools of the nuclear scientist—radiation detectors, nuclear reactors, and particle accelerators. In the preceding chapter, the principal research interests of nuclear chemists—nuclear spectroscopy and nuclear reactions—were studied. However, most chemists who use radioisotopes are not nuclear chemists. To these latter, radioactivity is a tool to be used in chemical research in somewhat the same fashion as spectrometry. The nuclear chemist uses chemical techniques to study nuclear phenomena, whereas the radiochemist uses nuclear techniques to study chemical phenomena. In this chapter we shall review some of the ways in which radiochemistry has aided research in analytical, inorganic, organic, and physical chemistry.

7–1 Basic Assumptions for Tracer Use

There are two reasons for using radioisotopes in chemical research. Some answers can *only* be obtained through the use of tracers; for example, self-diffusion of metal ions in solutions of their salts cannot be studied in any other fashion. In cases where the use of tracers is not necessary in principle, however, it may still be justified by its greater convenience than other techniques. The study of coprecipitation is such a case. Although corresponding answers can be obtained through stable isotope tracer investigations (e.g., using deuterium rather than tritium) followed by mass spectrometric analysis, it is normally far simpler to use radioactive tracers followed by counting. For those elements such as He, Li, B, N, and O for which no radioactive isotope of suitable half-life exists, the stable isotope technique must, of course, be employed.

There are two assumptions implicit in the use of radioisotopes. It is assumed that radioactive isotopes are chemically identical with stable isotopes of the same element: that the substitution of Co^{60} for Co^{59} in a compound of cobalt does not change the type or strength of the chemical bonds nor does it affect the physicial properties. The validity of this assumption depends on the precision of measurement of the chemical and physical properties. The difference in mass between the various isotopes does cause some change in these properties. This is true whether both isotopes are stable, both radioactive, or one stable and one radioactive. However, this isotope effect is rather small and is exceedingly difficult to detect, even for C^{14} and C^{12} where the mass difference is about 15 per cent. In practice, it is usually only necessary to consider isotope effects for the hydrogen-deuterium-tritium substitutions where large relative mass differences are involved.

The second assumption is that the radioactive nature of the isotope does not change the chemical or physical properties. Until the moment of its disintegration, the radioactive atom is indistinguishable from the stable atom except for the isotopic mass difference. Consequently, the only changes result from the small isotope effect described in the previous paragraph. Upon disintegration the atom is counted. Thereafter it is no longer the same element, and its subsequent chemical behavior is usually of no interest. As the rate of disintegration increases, the release of energetic radiations may cause secondary effects, as discussed in Sec. 3-1. In the well-designed tracer experiment, however, the level of radioactivity is high enough to provide accurate data but not high enough to produce noticeable radiation effects.

It would be a herculean task to attempt discussion of even a significant fraction of the uses of radioisotopes in the physical sciences. Instead we shall have to content ourselves with the discussion of a few examples chosen to indicate the utility of this technique.

ANALYTICAL CHEMISTRY

7–2 Radiometric Analysis

A simple, rapid analysis of inorganic systems may be performed by adding a slight excess of radioactive reagent to a solution of the unknown to quantitatively precipitate the latter. For example, to analyze for $Zn(II)$, an excess amount of a solution of $(NH_4)_2HP^*O_4$ labeled with P^{32} is added to the solution of zinc ions (Fig. 7–1). The $ZnNH_4P^*O_4$ precipitate that forms is filtered, washed, and counted for P^{32} activity. If the count rate per gram of phosphate in the $(NH_4)_2HP^*O_4$ solution is known, the observed count rate of the $ZnNH_4P^*O_4$ can be used to calculate the weight of phosphorus and hence the weight of $Zn(II)$ in the precipitate. No weighing of the final precipitate is required, nor is a high degree of chemical purity necessary in the precipitate; consequently, the analysis is quite rapid. Its accuracy is dependent on the accuracy of the counting step, the error usually being slightly less than 0.5 per cent. This procedure may be used for the quantitative analysis of a number of inorganic cations and anions.

Since radiometric analysis is so simple and rapid and the chemical purity of the counting sample relatively unimportant, it is very useful for checking yields of the various steps in a complicated analytical or synthetic process. In the analysis of fission-product yields, it is often necessary to perform a series of chemical separations, isolating various elements in each step. If, for example, the Ce^{144} present is to be removed from a fission-product mixture *after* the isolation of Pd, Sr, La, etc., the radiochemist tests for the loss of Ce^{144} in each of the steps prior to Ce^{144} isolation by adding a known amount of Ce^{144} activity in a trial run and going

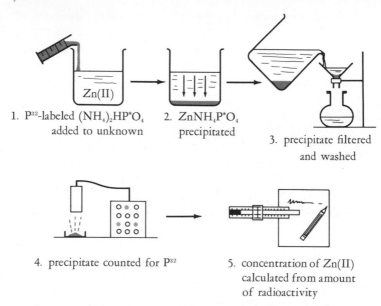

1. P^{32}-labeled $(NH_4)_2HP^*O_4$ 2. $ZnNH_4P^*O_4$
   added to unknown   precipitated

3. precipitate filtered
   and washed

4. precipitate counted for P^{32} 5. concentration of Zn(II)
                                           calculated from amount
                                           of radioactivity

Figure 7–1   Steps involved in the radiometric analysis of an unknown concentration of Zn(II) ions by use of a solution of P^{32}-labeled $(NH_4)_2HPO_4$.

through his procedure with inactive Pd, Sr, La, etc. The fractions isolated in each step are counted for Ce^{144} activity as is the over-all yield of Ce^{144} in the final cerium-isolation step. If one step shows a larger than desirable cerium loss, it can then be either improved or replaced. Furthermore, since very low levels of contamination can be measured by virtue of the sensitivity of the technique to low levels of radioactivity, tracers of Pd, Sr, La, etc., in the absence of radioactive cerium, can be used in additional test runs to determine the amounts of these elements present in the final isolated-cerium sample. The same trial processes can be carried out to check yield and contamination for each of the fission products to be isolated. Such use of tracers to ascertain yield and purity of each step has been of great help in industrial as well as laboratory processes.

The sensivity of tracer detection also makes measurement of the solubilities of relatively insoluble compounds rather simple. Chromatography, distillation, electrodeposition, extraction, precipitation, and coprecipitation are some of the techniques employed in analytical chemistry that have been studied with tracers.

7–3 Isotope Dilution

A very widely used technique, somewhat different in concept, is that of **isotope dilution**. It has been of considerable value in the analysis of complex mixtures of organic compounds. A small, pure radioactive sample of the desired component is added to the mixture to be analyzed. The mixture is then separated by a process designed to isolate the desired compound in high purity but not necessarily in high yield. The separated compound is weighed and accurately counted so that its specific activity (counts per minute per gram) can be calculated (Fig. 7–2). If the specific activity of the added sample is also known, the weight of the desired compound present in the original mixture, W_i, is calculated by the equation

$$W_i = \left[\frac{A_i}{A_f} - 1\right]W_f \qquad (7-1)$$

W_f is the weight of the final (separated) sample and A_i and A_f the specific activities of the added sample and the final sample, respectively. The basic purpose of the isotope-dilution technique is the determination of the chemical yield of the desired compound in a complex mixture; consequently, this technique is of particular advantage where quantitative separation of the desired compound is not feasible. In some cases, the measurement of the final sample utilizes a technique other than weighing but the principle remains the same. Problem 3 is an example of the use of isotope dilution in a practical laboratory situation.

7–4 Activation Analysis

The formation of radioactive nuclides by the capture of neutrons is the basis of activation analysis, a technique that continues

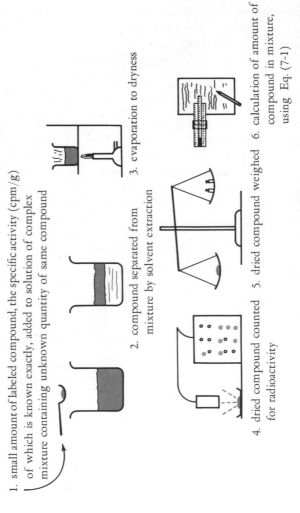

1. small amount of labeled compound, the specific activity (cpm/g) of which is known exactly, added to solution of complex mixture containing unknown quantity of same compound

2. compound separated from mixture by solvent extraction

3. evaporation to dryness

4. dried compound counted for radioactivity

5. dried compound weighed

6. calculation of amount of compound in mixture, using Eq. (7-1)

Figure 7-2 Possible sequence of steps for determining the amount of one compound in a complex mixture by the technique of isotope dilution.

to grow rapidly in importance. The cross section for thermal neutron capture varies widely from one nuclide to another. If an impurity has a large cross section for production of a rather short-lived nuclide, it can frequently be measured in impurity levels of less than one part per billion. It may be necessary to separate out the radioactivity by chemical means after irradiation, but such separation is often unnecessary, particularly if the radioactivity has gamma-ray emission associated with it. In many instances more than one radioactive species is formed, and successful use of the technique may *depend* on gamma spectrometry. If three nuclides are formed that emit gamma rays of 0.2, 0.5, and 0.7 MeV, respectively, it is possible by gamma spectrometry to discriminate against any two and determine the count rate and half-life of the third.

The sensitivities of some elements to neutron-activation analysis are listed in Table 7–1 for a neutron flux of 10^{12} neutrons/cm²/sec. The sensitivity increases with an increase in neutron flux, an increase in cross section, and a decrease in half-life. Once the decay rate of the sample is measured, the amount of the impurity can be calculated by use of proper values for the cross section, neutron flux, irradiation time, and half-life. However, a simpler approach has been developed that avoids errors implicit in the uncertainty of each of these values. The unknown and a known standard of

Table 7–1
Sensitivity to Neutron-Activation Analysis
(neutron flux, 10^{12} neutrons/cm²/sec)

Grams	Elements
10^{-11}–10^{-12}	Eu, Dy
10^{-10}–10^{-11}	In, Ir, Mn, Sm
10^{-9}–10^{-10}	Cu, Na, W, Ta, Sb
10^{-8}–10^{-9}	Ge, Se, Ni, Zn, Co
10^{-7}–10^{-8}	Ag, Sn, Zr, Hg, Cr
10^{-6}–10^{-7}	Bi, Ca, Fe, S, Si

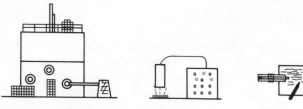

1. known and unknown samples placed   2. both samples counted   3. calculation of unknown
    in nuclear reactor together   in identical fashion   concentration, using
                                                                     Eq. (7-2)

**Figure 7–3   Determination of the amount of an impurity
in a sample, using the matched-sample technique of neutron-activation analysis.**

similar composition are irradiated and counted in identical fashion
(Fig. 7–3). A direct comparison can then be made according to
the following relationship:

$$\frac{\text{weight of impurity in unknown}}{\text{weight of impurity in standard}} = \frac{\text{activity of impurity in unknown}}{\text{activity of impurity in standard}}$$

$$(7\text{–}2)$$

Analyses of trace constituents in water, in soil, and in marine
and biological systems are only a few of the interesting determina-
tions facilitated by neutron-activation analysis. It can be ascertained, for example, in which county in Virginia a tobacco
sample has been grown by analysis of its trace constituents. Activation analysis of the mineral content of pigments has enabled
scientists to determine the authenticity of paintings attributed to
certain artists since, in times past, each artist prepared his own
paints by distinctive and individual formulae. An activation analysis that once attracted some public notice indicated that
Napoleon may have died from arsenic poisoning. As scientists in
many disciplines become familiar with the technique of activation
analysis, further interesting applications will undoubtedly result.

PHYSICAL AND INORGANIC CHEMISTRY

Our understanding of physical and inorganic chemistry has been considerably increased by research using radiochemical techniques. The fields of molecular structure, reaction kinetics, catalysis, surface reactions, and diffusion in gases, liquids, and solids have effectively exploited the use of tracers on an ever-broadening scale. Let us consider briefly a few examples of these researches to illustrate the types of results obtained through radiochemistry.

7-5   Reaction Kinetics and Mechanisms

Both Fe(II) and Fe(III) can exist simultaneously in a solution. It was of interest to know if the two oxidation states are in dynamic equilibrium and how conversion from one state to the other occurs. To study this exchange, inactive Fe(III) ions were mixed in solution with radioactive Fe(II) ions. The activity was observed to distribute itself evenly between the two oxidation states, indicating the presence of a dynamic exchange represented by

$$Fe(III) + Fe^*(II) \rightleftarrows Fe^*(III) + Fe(II) \qquad (7\text{-}3)$$

In this exchange, an electron is transferred from an active Fe(II) ion to an inactive Fe(III), with the result that the active ion acquires an oxidation state of III whereas the inactive ion is reduced to the II state. Obviously, since the radioactivity cannot be transferred, the ions exchange their respective oxidation states. It is unlikely that a dipositive Fe* (II) and a tripositive Fe (III) can approach each other close enough to exchange an electron directly, for they experience a coulombic repulsion just as do a proton and a positive nucleus. A more likely mechanism is that an anion is used as a bridge. The intrusion of the anion reduces the coulombic repulsion; not only because it increases the distance of nearest approach for the two positive ions but also because it introduces a negative anionic charge. If an anion bridge is indeed used, the reaction mechanism might be represented

$$Fe(III) + X^- + Fe^*(II) \rightleftarrows (Fe^*\!\!-\!\!X\!\!-\!\!Fe)^{4+} \rightleftarrows Fe(II)$$
$$+ X^- + Fe^*(III) \qquad (7\text{-}4)$$

By using radioactive iodine as a tracer, it has been demonstrated that the I_2-I^- exchange occurs via the triiodide ion I_3^-. The mechanism is

$$I^- + I—I^* \rightleftarrows (I—I—I^*)^- \rightleftarrows I—I + I^{*-} \qquad (7-5)$$

Another electron-transfer system in which an anion-bridge mechanism seems to be involved is Cr^{++}–$[Co(NH_3)_5Cl]^{++}$. When radioactive chloride was used in the $[Co(NH_3)_5Cl]^{++}$ ion, the $CrCl^{++}$ product was found to have radioactivity, suggesting the mechanism to be

$$Cr^{++} + [Co(NH_3)_5Cl^*]^{++} \rightleftarrows (Cr—Cl^*—Co)^{4+} \rightleftarrows CrCl^{*++}$$

$$+ Co(NH_3)_5^{++} \qquad (7-6)$$

It was possible that another anionic solute species served as the bridge and that the transfer of active chloride from cobalt to chromium was not directly involved in the electron-transfer reaction. To check this possibility, the same reaction was carried out without active chloride in the cobalt complex but with active chloride ions in the solution. When the reaction was performed rapidly, no active chloride was found in the $CrCl^{++}$ species, showing that the oxidation proceeded with the transfer of chloride from cobalt to chromium but without involvement of other solute anions. Only the ability to demonstrate by use of tracers that the chloride ions in $CrCl^{++}$ came directly from the cobalt complex and not from the solution made it possible to choose Eq. (7–6) as the probable mechanism.

7–6 Structural Studies

Exchange studies have also been used to obtain information on the structure of molecules. A typical example of the very large number of such investigations involved the thiocyanate ion. In the thiosulfate ion $(S_2O_3)^=$, the two sulfurs could have been in a similar structural condition—e.g., $(O—S—O—S—O)^=$—or in nonequivalent positions—e.g., $(S—SO_3)^=$. With radioactive sulfur, it was possible to choose unambiguously between these two possibilities. If active sulfur is added to a sulfite solution, active thiosulfate is formed. Decomposition of this thiosulfate by acidification into sulfur dioxide would result in activity in both SO_2 and S^0 if the first alternative structure were correct but only in the S^0 if the second were correct. Since all the activity appeared in the free sulfur, the nonequivalent structure was proved accurate and the over-all structural reaction was shown to be

$$
\begin{bmatrix} O & & O \\ & \diagdown S \diagup & \\ & \| & \\ & O & \end{bmatrix}^{=} + S^* \rightarrow \begin{bmatrix} O & & O \\ & \diagdown S \diagup & \\ O \diagup & & \diagdown S^* \end{bmatrix}^{=} \xrightarrow{2H^+} H_2O + S \diagup\!\!\!\!\diagdown {}^{O}_{O} + S^*
$$

(7-7)

7-7 Diffusion Studies

Unless tracers are used, it is not possible to prove that the iron ions in a solution containing Fe(II) and Fe(III) are in actuality continuously shifting between the two oxidation states in a dynamic equilibrium. The same inability to distinguish changes between identical atoms requires the use of tracers to study the phenomena of self-diffusion. Using O^{18}- and H^3-labeled water, the rate of diffusion of H_2O in water has been measured. The results are interpreted as confirming the theory of the semicrystalline nature of liquid water, in which many H_2O molecules are connected by hydrogen bonds to four other water molecules in a tetrahedral structure.

Interesting and valuable data have been collected on the rates of diffusion of atoms in metals. The self-diffusions of Au* in gold, Cu* in copper, Zn* in zinc, and Ag* in silver have been studied. The diffusion of Bi* in bismuth metal is especially interesting in that a difference by a factor of 100,000 has been shown to exist between its diffusion rates in two mutually perpendicular directions. Another example of the type of information obtained is the fact that Pb* diffuses 100,000 times slower than Au* and 10 times slower than Sn* in solid lead. The diffusion rates of ions in crystals as well as those of ions in molten salts and in solutions have been determined by tracer techniques. These diffusion results have aided considerably in the development of improved theories on the natures of metals, liquids, crystals, and solutions.

7-8 Artificial Elements

Some of the artificial elements have been available only in very small amounts since their initial preparations. For elements such as Tc, Pm, At, Fr, and Np through Lw, a great amount of chemical information has necessarily been gained by tracer experimentation. The experimental discovery of element 101, mendelevium, is a good example of work done in this field. Approximately 10^9 atoms (an invisible and unweighable amount) of $_{99}Es^{253}$ was electrodeposited on a small area of a thin gold foil. The Es^{253} had been prepared by long-term neutron irradiation of Pu^{239} in a reactor, as described in Chap. VI. Es^{253} is an alpha emitter with a 20-day half-life, so the amount deposited on the gold foil could be ascertained by alpha counting. The Es^{253} target was bombarded in a cyclotron with alpha particles of about 40-MeV energy. A **recoil technique** was used so that the alpha particles hit the Es atoms *after* passage through the gold foil. This allowed the atoms of element 101 that were formed to be knocked out of the target and caught on another thin gold foil (Fig. 7–4). It was possible by this technique to obtain the mendelevium atoms without destroying the einsteinium target after each bombardment. The gold "recoil-catcher" foil was removed and subjected to several chemical processes to purify and isolate the mendelevium. The foil was dissolved in aqua regia; the resulting solution, adjusted to 8 M in HCl, was then passed through an anion-exchange resin column where the gold was retained on the resin as the $AuCl_4^-$ anion. Since the mendelevium atoms immediately passed through the resin bed that absorbed anions from solution, it was possible to conclude that mendelevium does not form strong anionic complexes with chloride ions. It was found, however, that mendelevium could be coprecipitated with $La(OH)_3$ or LaF_3, indicating that $Md(OH)_3$ and MdF_3 are comparatively insoluble. Finally, the mendelevium ions were dissolved in a solution of α-hydroxyisobutyrate, $(CH_3)_2C(OH)CO_2^-$, a good complexing agent. The resulting solution was passed through a cation-exchange resin column, and the actinides were removed in the order shown in Fig. 7–5. The elution data, plotted in the figure, prove that mendelevium forms a stronger complex than fermium, einsteinium, or californium. Since the type and strength of the californium isobutyrate complexes have been studied, reliable estimates of the corresponding data for mendelevium can be made.

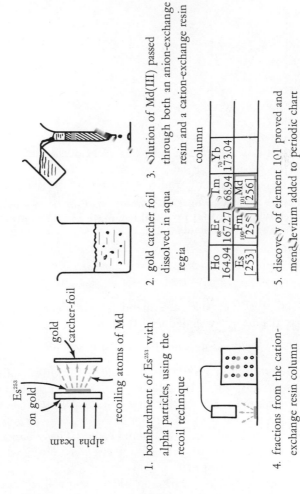

Es^{253} on gold

gold catcher-foil

alpha beam

recoiling atoms of Md

gold catcher foil dissolved in aqua regia

1. bombardment of Es^{253} with alpha particles, using the recoil technique

2. gold catcher foil dissolved in aqua regia

3. solution of Md(III) passed through both an anion-exchange resin and a cation-exchange resin column

4. fractions from the cation-exchange resin column counted

5. discovery of element 101 proved and mendelevium added to periodic chart

Ho 164.94	$_{68}$Er 167.27	$_{69}$Tm 168.94	$_{70}$Yb 173.04
Es [253]	$_{100}$Fm [25?]	$_{101}$Md [256]	

Figure 7–4 Steps involved in the formation and isolation of mendelevium.

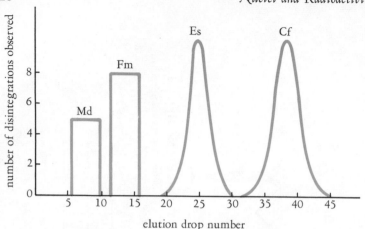

elution drop number

Figure 7–5   Data obtained during elution from a cation-exchange resin that provided the main chemical proof for the discovery of element 101.

From the fact that the mendelevium decayed by electron capture to Fm^{256}, it was deduced that the production reaction was

$$_{99}Es^{253} + {}_2He^4 \rightarrow {}_{101}Md^{256} + n \qquad (7\text{-}8)$$

With the amount of Es^{253} available and the intensity of the alpha beam used, only one or two atoms of Md^{256} could be made per hour of bombardment.   Initial isolation and identification were accomplished with a total of 13 atoms of Md^{256}, resulting from three successive bombardments of 3 hours each.   The chemical data on the chloride and isobutyrate complexes were obtained with this same small number of atoms.

In similar fashion, with the aid of coprecipitation, solvent-extraction, and ion-exchange techniques, extensive data have been accumulated on the solubilities of compounds, the oxidation states, and the types and strengths of complexes characteristic of these artificial elements.   Even though macro amounts of many of them are now available, the high level of radioactivity associated with ~ge samples often causes serious side effects.   These side effects result from radiolysis of the components of the solution. Consequently, if one wishes to study, for example, the physical-chemical properties of californium as element 98 and without perturbation by any radiolytic effects, it may still be advantageous and perhaps even necessary to use tracer techniques. At tracer levels, the radiolysis is too slight to be a perturbing factor.

ORGANIC AND BIOLOGICAL CHEMISTRY

The three radioactive tracers of greatest importance in these fields of chemistry are H^3, C^{14}, and S^{35}. Unfortunately, all three of these nuclides are beta emitters of low energy, and as a result reliable counting becomes a serious problem. For C^{14}-labeling, a common technique is to oxidize the organic compound to C^*O_2 and count the latter in the gaseous state. Liquid scintillation counting, as well as proportional and Geiger counting for solid samples, are also used.

7–9 Organic Reactions

The use of tracers in organic analysis has been discussed in Sec. 7–3 on isotope dilution. The tracer technique has also been invaluable in elucidating mechanisms of organic reactions. As an example we may consider the reaction between organic acids and alcohols to form esters, since its mechanism was definitely established from the results of tracer experiments. The reaction is written

$$\text{organic acid} + \text{alcohol} \rightarrow \text{ester} + \text{water}$$

$$R-C\underset{\diagdown OH}{\overset{\diagup O}{}} + H-O-R' \rightarrow R-C\underset{\diagdown O-R'}{\overset{\diagup O}{}} + H_2O \quad \text{(7–9)}$$

where R and R' represent hydrocarbon groups such as CH_3, C_2H_5, C_3H_7, etc. Although this looks like an acid-base reaction, it ha been shown that the mechanism actually involves the OH of the acid and the H of the alcohol in the following way:

$$R—C\diagup_{\diagdown O^*—H}^{O} \boxed{+ H}—O—R' \rightarrow R—C\diagup_{\diagdown O—R'}^{O} + H_2O^* \qquad (7\text{--}10)$$

Since the organic compound may be decomposed during a reaction, one must make certain that the labeled atom is in the proper position to be useful. In the acid-alcohol reaction, the mechanism would not have been elucidated if the carbon atom had been labeled—i.e., R—C*OOH. It was necessary to label the OH oxygen either of the acid or of the alcohol.

Three syntheses of acetic acid will indicate how different positions may be labeled.

1. *Acetic acid—2—C¹⁴*

$$BaC^*O_3 \xrightarrow{HCl} C^*O_2 \xrightarrow[\text{catalyst}]{H_2} C^*H_3OH \xrightarrow{PI_3}$$

$$C^*H_3I \xrightarrow{KCN} C^*H_3CN \xrightarrow{H_2O} C^*H_3CO_2H \qquad (7\text{--}11)$$

2. *Acetic acid—1—C¹⁴*

$$BaC^*O_3 \xrightarrow{HCl} C^*O_2 \xrightarrow{CH_3MgBr} CH_3C^*O_2H \qquad (7\text{--}12)$$

3. *Acetic acid—1,2—C¹⁴*

$$BaC^*O_3 \xrightarrow[\Delta]{Mg} BaC^*_2 \xrightarrow{H_2O} C^*_2H_2 \xrightarrow[\text{catalyst}]{H_2O}$$

$$C^*H_3C^*HO \xrightarrow{[O]} C^*H_3C^*O_2H \qquad (7\text{--}13)$$

7–10 Photosynthesis

In medicine and biochemistry, the great advances of the last decade would have been much delayed without the aid of tracer techniques. The usefulness of radioisotopes in diagnosing and treating disease is reflected by the fact that over 50,000 patients are administered radioisotopes each year in the United States. Heart disease, cancer, the roles of vitamins and hormones, and metabolism are only a few of the areas in which tracers have benefited medical science. The knowledge of the mode, the rate, and the extent of uptake of nutrients, water, and minerals by plants and organisms as determined by tracers has added much to our understanding of basic biochemical processes. One of the major triumphs of the tracer technique was the solving of the mystery of photosynthesis by Melvin Calvin.

All life ultimately depends on the process of photosynthesis, in which the energy of sunlight is converted into chemical energy by plants. The conversion occurs with reduction of the carbon dioxide absorbed by the plant from the atmosphere and liberation of oxygen into the atmosphere. Thus photosynthesis reverses the oxygen-consumption processes of burning and breathing and serves to maintain the $O_2 : CO_2$ ratio of the atmosphere. The over-all process can be represented

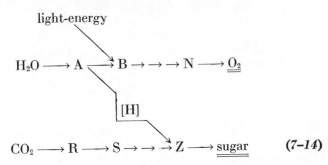

$$\text{(7-14)}$$

or

$$6CO_2 + 6H_2O \rightarrow 6O_2 + C_6H_{12}O_6(\text{sugar})$$

This scheme indicates that light energy reacts with H_2O, which is reduced via the intermediate states A, B, C, etc. to O_2. During this process, "active" hydrogen is released and interacts somewhere along the CO_2 chain . . . X → Y → Z to result eventually in the formation of a sugar (a carbohydrate) and water. To determine the exact path of the process, it was necessary to identify which of the very many chemical substances in plants correspond to the intermediate molecules, A, B, . . . , N and R, S, . . . , Z. Calvin's research group placed plants into atmospheres containing C^{14}- labeled CO_2 so as to allow the C^*O_2 to enter the leaves in

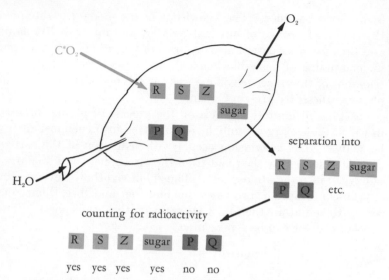

Figure 7-6   Method used by Calvin to determine which of the compounds in a leaf were involved in photosynthesis.

the photosynthetic cycle. Photosynthesis was stopped by killing the plant, and from it the scientists then proceeded to separate as many molecular components as possible. These separated compounds were tested for radioactivity (Fig. 7–6). Appearance of C^{14} activity was taken as proof that the compound was involved in the process of photosynthesis. Tritium was used in the same way to confirm the sequence suggested by the C^{14} data.

The results of these experiments were interpreted by Calvin to indicate the following mechanism. CO_2 enters the leaf and combines with sugar, thereby forming an acid. The sunlight, using chlorophyll as a catalyst, reacts with H_2O to release oxygen and an active hydrogen. The latter reduces the acid to a sugar and this in turn undergoes a series of molecular rearrangements to revert to the original sugar and thereby complete the cycle. In each cycle a new molecule of the sugar ($C_6H_{12}O_6$) and six molecules of O_2 are formed from six molecules each of CO_2 and H_2O.

7–11 Radioisotope Dating

Although C^{14} has a half-life of only 5568 years, its concentration in the atmosphere as C^*O_2 remains constant. This is the result of a reaction

$$N^{14} + n \rightarrow C^{14} + p \qquad (7-15)$$

that is constantly occurring with neutrons released by cosmic ray action. Living organisms establish equilibrium with atmospheric CO_2, so that the specific activity for C^{14} per gram of carbon is identical in living organisms and in the atmosphere. Death halts the exchange between the organism and the atmosphere and thus destroys the equilibrium. After death, no new C^{14} is added to the organism and the amount present decreases in accord with the 5568-year half-life. Measurement of the specific activity of C^{14} for such a dead organism provides a means of calculating the time since its death. The specific activity in the atmosphere or in living trees and animal tissue everywhere in the world is approximately 15 beta disintegrations per min per g. Measurement of the C^{14} activity in a cypress beam in the tomb of Egyptian Pharaoh Sneferu (Fig. 7–7) gave 8 disintegrations per min, indicating that the tomb has an age slightly less than one half-life for C^{14} (5568 years). This tomb is known to date from about 2600 B.C., agreement that is quite acceptable. Objects as old as 30,000 years have been similarly dated. In 1960 Willard Libby received the Nobel Prize for his role in the development of the C^{14} dating method. Libby has also shown that tritium (H^3) can be used to date such objects as wine or water up to ages of 25 to 30 years. Tritium dating has indicated the layer of water at the bottom of the ocean to be quite a bit older than that at the surface. This is believed to mean that the mixing of the ocean waters is not particularly rapid. Tritium in surface water is in equilibrium with atmospheric tritium whereas water at the sea bottom is out of contact with atmospheric tritium. Water dating by tritium has also been used to ascertain how long spring waters have been underground.

A simple equation for calculating radiocarbon dates is

$$t = 1.85 \times 10^4 \log (15.3/D) \qquad (7-16$$

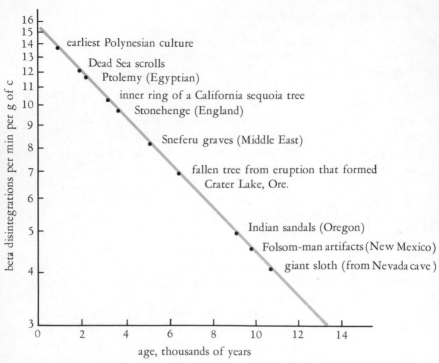

Figure 7–7   Some of the archeological objects dated by C¹⁴.

where t is the age of the sample and D is its specific activity in disintegrations per min per g.

INDUSTRY AND AGRICULTURE

Before we conclude this chapter on the uses of radioisotopes in chemistry, some mention should be made of their use by industry and agriculture. It was estimated in 1953 that radioisotopes were saving U.S. industry approximately one hundred million dollars a year. By 1957 this estimate had risen to four hundred million dollars annually. ‚ubsequent increase in the variety of applications has caused a continued

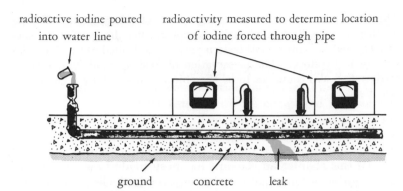

radioactive iodine poured   radioactivity measured to determine location
into water line   of iodine forced through pipe

ground   concrete   leak

**Figure 7–8   Schematic diagram of the use of I^{131} to detect
leaks in water lines.**

increase in their value to industry.   Radioisotopes are used both as tracers
and as sealed radiation sources.   As tracers, they are used to measure
friction wear, solid diffusion, detergency, and mineral flotation; to study
the role of catalysts; to trace the flow of liquids through pipes; and to
follow the paths of compounds in a multistep process (e.g., dye migration
in a multicolor printing process).   Fig. 7–8 illustrates the use of I^{131} to
locate leaks in a pipe line.   Since I^{131} has an 8-day half-life, the radioactivity rather quickly disappears after serving its purpose.   The tracer
technique is more convenient and economical than other techniques when
buried pipes are involved since it does not necessitate removal of flooring
and the like.

As radiation sources, beta emitters are being used for quality control
and as thickness gauges in cigarette manufacture, paper milling, and
plastic and metal production.   Radiation sources also find extensive appli-
cation in the preparation of metal-casting radiographs to reveal slight
cracks or structural flaws.   It is possible that large-scale use may be made
of radiation sources in the future to increase the amount of cross-linking
in polyethylene and thus produce a more elastic and heat-resistant plastic.

In agriculture, radiation can be used to multiply considerably the
possibilities for genetic changes in plants.   New and improved species
may be selected from the resulting mutants.   An improved variety of
peanut is now in commercial production as a consequence of such irradiations.   A new variety of bush bean, one that produces 30 per cent more
than its parent variety and matures more rapidly, is also on the market.

Bibliography

Below are listed some references for additional reading in nuclear and radiochemistry.

B. G. Harvey, *Introduction to Nuclear Physics and Chemistry*, Prentice-Hall, Englewood Cliffs, N.J., 1962.

G. Friedlander and J. Kennedy, *Nuclear and Radiochemistry*, Wiley, New York, 1955.

R. E. Lapp and H. L. Andrews, *Nuclear Radiation Physics*, Prentice-Hall, Englewood Cliffs, N.J., 1954.

S. Glasstone, *Sourcebook on Atomic Energy*, Van Nostrand, Princeton, N.J., 1950.

R. R. Williams, *Principles of Nuclear Chemistry*, Van Nostrand, Princeton, N.J., 1950.

D. Halliday, *Introductory Nuclear Physics*, Wiley, New York, 1955.

R. D. Evans, *The Atomic Nucleus*, McGraw-Hill, New York, 1955.

G. R. Choppin, *Experimental Nuclear Chemistry*, Prentice-Hall, Englewood Cliffs, N.J., 1961.

R. T. Overman and H. M. Clark, *Radioisotope Techniques*, McGraw-Hill, New York, 1960.

A. C. Wahl and N. A. Bonner, *Radioactivity Applied to Chemistry*, Wiley, New York, 1951.

W. B. Fretter, *Introduction to Experimental Physics*, Prentice-Hall, Englewood Cliffs, N.J., 1954.

W. J. Price, *Nuclear Radiation Detection*, McGraw-Hill, New York, 1958.

E. Bleuler and G. J. Goldsmith, *Experimental Nucleonics*, Holt, Rinehart, and Winston, New York, 1952.

M. Calvin et al., *Isotopic Carbon*, Wiley, New York, 1949.

J. G. Burr, *Tracer Applications for the Study of Organic Reactions*, Wiley-Interscience, New York, 1957.

J. R. Bradford, *Radioisotopes in Industry*, Reinhold, New York, 1953.

Appendix A

Biological Effects of Radiation

Atomic energy and nuclear weapons are so much a part of our present-day world that it is exceedingly rare to find an issue of a daily newspaper that does not include one or more stories on the subject. A large number of these news stories have reported the world-wide debate over the inherent dangers of radioactive fallout. With such constant publicity, it is not surprising that many laymen consider radiation and radioisotope research extremely hazardous. It is quite true that radiation always represents a danger to biological systems. However, as in all matters, the level of danger is directly proportional to the extent of an individual's ignorance. We are constantly surrounded by danger—automobiles improperly handled, drugs taken in overdoses, even certain sports. These dangers are accepted because the benefits that accrue to mankind in general from the proper use of drugs, from sports, and from automobiles are considered to outweigh their disadvantages. Similarly, the danger from radiation must be accepted as a necessary evil in order to achieve a greater good. The danger is minimized by proper precautions and safety measures, in much the same way that dangers attending the use of strong acids, hydrogen sulfide gas, and other toxic chemicals in the chemistry laboratory are minimized. Since radioactivity can be detected in extremely small amounts by monitor instruments, safety is often much less a problem in a radiochemical laboratory than it is in a general chemical laboratory where safety rules are apt to be less rigorously followed.

It will be necessary to observe several human generations before scientists can reach conclusive agreement over the total effect of radiation on man. However, much is already known, and a general basis for biologi-

137

cal radiation damage has been established. As radiation traverses a biological system, it loses energy by causing ionization and excitation of atoms and molecules as was discussed in Sec. 3–1. The direct rupture by radiation of chemical bonds in a cell can damage or kill the cell. Moreover, radiation reacts with water both inside and outside the cell to form free radicals—chemical species of great reactivity. These free radicals in turn do extensive cell damage by causing oxidation-reduction reactions. Although the different radiations differ in the extent to which they produce these effects, they all produce the same types. The actual extent of biological damage depends on such factors as the type and energy of the radiation, the rate of its administration, the organ of the body irradiated, and the age and general health of the person irradiated. Since young, growing cells are more susceptible to damage than adult cells, it is advisable to prevent unnecessary exposure to radiation of anyone below 18 years of age. On the other hand, because cancer cells are in a state of rapid growth, they are more susceptible to damage by radiation than are normal cells. This is the basis for the radiation treatment of cancer. The blood-forming organs (spleen, bone marrow, etc.) are also particularly susceptible to damage.

These variables make it impossible to state that a certain definite amount of radiation or number of disintegrations will produce a certain definite effect in an individual person. However, we must consider that radiation is always damaging to some extent. The body has the ability to recover from most radiation effects, but there is definite proof of the occurrence of residual effects that may appear much later in the form of cancer, genetic mutations, or acceleration of the aging process. To illustrate the small magnitude of these long-term effects, we should point out that a person who received the maximum permissible amount (by Atomic Energy Commission regulations) of radiation every week for 20 years would shorten his life expectancy by only 1 year. This is an extremely unlikely situation; exposure to even 1/100 the permissible amount over 20 years is rather unlikely.

Appendix B

Table of Isotopes

A number of radioisotopes with $Z < 85$ used frequently in scientific research are listed below together with their half-lives and modes of decay. Since over 1200 radioactive nuclides are known, these represent a rather small percentage of the total. The energies listed are the maximum beta energies; for both beta and gamma rays, only those in at least 5 per cent abundance are given. For a more complete listing of isotopes and their properties, see the Table of Isotopes in *Reviews of Modern Physics*.[1]

Element	Isotope	Half-life	E_β, MeV	E_γ, MeV
Tritium	$_1H^3$	12.3 y	0.018	none
Beryllium	$_4Be^7$	53.5 d	E.C.	0.478, X rays
Carbon	$_6C^{14}$	5568 y	0.155	none
Fluorine	$_9F^{18}$	112 m	$0.64(\beta^+)$	none
Sodium	$_{11}Na^{22}$	2.6 y	$0.54(\beta^+)$	1.28
	$_{11}Na^{24}$	15.0 h	1.40	1.37, 2.75
Magnesium	$_{12}Mg^{28}$	21.2 h	0.42	0.032, 0.40, 0.95, 1.35
Phosphorus	$_{15}P^{32}$	14.3 d	1.71	none
Sulfur	$_{16}S^{35}$	87 d	0.168	none

[1] D. Strominger, J. M. Hollander, and G. T. Seaborg, *Rev. Mod. Phys.*, **30**, 585 (1958).

Element	Isotope	Half-life	E_β, MeV	E_γ, MeV
Chlorine	$_{17}Cl^{36}$	3×10^5 y	0.71	none
Potassium	$_{19}K^{42}$	12.5 h	2.00	1.53
Calcium	$_{20}Ca^{45}$	164 d	0.255	none
Scandium	$_{21}Sc^{46}$	84 d	0.36	0.89, 1.12
Vanadium	$_{23}V^{48}$	16 d	0.694(β^+)	0.986, 1.314
			E.C.	X rays
Chromium	$_{24}Cr^{51}$	27.8 d	E.C.	0.325, X rays
Manganese	$_{25}Mn^{52}$	5.7 d	0.58(β^+)	0.73, 0.94, 1.46
Iron	$_{26}Fe^{55}$	2.6 y	E.C.	none, X rays
	$_{26}Fe^{59}$	45.1 d	0.27	1.098
			0.46	1.289
Cobalt	$_{27}Co^{60}$	5.24 y	0.312	1.172, 1.332
Nickel	$_{28}Ni^{59}$	8×10^4 y	E.C.	none, X rays
	$_{28}Ni^{63}$	125 y	0.067	none
Copper	$_{29}Cu^{64}$	12.8 h	0.57(β^-)	none
			0.65(β^+)	X rays
			E.C.	
Zinc	$_{30}Zn^{65}$	245 d	E.C.	1.119, X rays
Gallium	$_{31}Ga^{72}$	14.3 h	0.64	0.601, 0.630
			0.96	0.834, 0.894
			1.51	1.050, 1.595
			2.53	1.859, 2.203
			3.17	2.491, 2.508
Germanium	$_{32}Ge^{71}$	11.4 d	E.C.	none, X rays
Arsenic	$_{33}As^{76}$	26.4 h	1.76	0.555
			2.41	0.648
			2.97	1.210
	$_{33}As^{77}$	38.7 h	0.68	none
Bromine	$_{35}Br^{82}$	35.9 h	0.444	0.554, 0.619, 0.698, 0.777, 0.828, 1.044, 1.317, 1.475
Rubidium	$_{37}Rb^{86}$	18.7 d	0.71, 1.78	1.08
Strontium	$_{38}Sr^{89}$	50.5 d	1.46	none
	$_{38}Sr^{90}$	27.7 y	0.545 (also Y^{90} radiations if present)	none

Element	Isotope	Half-life	E_β, MeV	E_γ, MeV
Yttrium	$_{39}Y^{90}$	64.2 h	2.26	none
	$_{39}Y^{91}$	57.5 d	1.54	none
Zirconium	$_{40}Zr^{95}$	65 d	0.360	0.722
			0.396	0.754
Niobium	$_{41}Nb^{95}$	35 d	0.158	0.765
Molybdenum	$_{42}Mo^{99}$	66.0 h	0.41, 1.18	0.140, 0.745,
				0.780, 0.850
Technetium	$_{43}Tc^{96}$	4.20 d	E.C.	0.771, 0.806,
				0.842, 1.119,
				X rays
	$_{43}Tc^{99}$	2.1×10^5 y	0.29	none
Ruthenium	$_{44}Ru^{106}$	1.00 y	0.039	none (Rh^{106}
				radiations)
Rhodium	$_{45}Rh^{103m}$	57 m	I.T.	0.040
	$_{45}Rh^{105}$	36.5 h	0.25, 0.56	0.32
	$_{45}Rh^{106}$	30 s	2.44, 3.1,	0.513, 0.624,
			3.53	1.045
Palladium	$_{46}Pd^{103}$	17.0 d	E.C.	0.040 (Rh^{103m}),
				0.298, 0.362,
				0.498,
				X rays
	$_{46}Pd^{109}$	13.5 h	1.03	0.087 (from
				40-sec Ag^{109m}
				daughter)
Silver	$_{47}Ag^{105}$	40 d	E.C.	0.064, 0.281,
				0.345, 0.443,
				0.654,
				X rays
	$_{47}Ag^{110m}$	253 d	0.087,	0.446, 0.657,
			0.530	0.677, 0.705,
				0.764, 0.817,
				0.884, 0.937,
				1.384, 1.504
	$_{47}Ag^{111}$	7.6 d	0.70, 1.04	0.243, 0.340
Cadmium	$_{48}Cd^{109}$	470 d	E.C.	0.087, X rays
Indium	$_{49}In^{114m}$	50 d	I.T.	0.190
	$_{49}In^{114}$	72 s	1.984	none
Tin	$_{50}Sn^{113}$	119 d	E.C.	0.260, 0.393

Element	Isotope	Half-life	E_β, MeV	E_γ, MeV
Antimony	$_{51}Sb^{124}$	60.9 d	0.24, 0.61, 0.97, 1.60, 2.32	0.603, 0.646, 0.723, 1.692
	$_{51}Sb^{125}$	2.0 y	0.128, 0.299, 0.444, 0.616	0.175, 0.43, 0.46, 0.60, 0.64
Tellurium	$_{52}Te^{127m}$	105 d	I.T.	0.089
	$_{52}Te^{127}$	9.4 h	0.70	none
Iodine	$_{53}I^{131}$	8.08 d	0.335, 0.608	0.284, 0.364, 0.637
Cesium	$_{55}Cs^{134}$	2.07 y	0.083, 0.655, 0.683	0.565, 0.570, 0.606, 0.797, 0.802
	$_{55}Cs^{137}$	26.6 y	0.51, 1.17	0.662
Barium	$_{56}Ba^{140}$	12.8 d	0.48, 1.02 (see La^{140})	0.030, 0.537
Lanthanum	$_{57}La^{140}$	40.2 h	0.42, 0.86, 1.15, 1.36, 1.62, 2.20	0.328, 0.438, 0.490, 0.815, 1.60
Cerium	$_{58}Ce^{141}$	33.1 d	0.442, 0.581	0.142
	$_{58}Ce^{144}$	285 d	0.175, 0.309	0.033, 0.042, 0.054, 0.081, 0.133 (also Pr^{144} radiations)
Praseodymium	$_{59}Pr^{143}$	13.7 d	0.932	none
	$_{59}Pr^{144}$	17.3 m	2.98	none
Promethium	$_{61}Pm^{147}$	2.64 y	0.223	none
Samarium	$_{62}Sm^{153}$	47.1 h	0.26, 0.69, 0.80	0.65, 0.72, 0.83
Europium	$_{63}Eu^{154}$	16 y	0.12, 0.25, 0.55, 0.83, 1.84	0.123, 0.725, 0.875, 0.998, 1.007, 1.227
	$_{63}Eu^{155}$	1.7 y	0.154, 0.243	0.0188, 0.0865, 0.1052
Thulium	$_{69}Tm^{170}$	129 d	0.884, 0.968	0.084

Element	*Isotope*	*Half-life*	E_β, *MeV*	E_γ, *MeV*
Hafnium	$_{72}Hf^{181}$	44.6 d	0.408	0.004, 0.133, 0.482
Tantalum	$_{73}Ta^{182}$	115 d	0.36, 0.44, 0.514	0.068, 0.100, 0.156, 0.179, 0.222, 0.229, 0.264, 1.122, 1.189, 1.222, 1.231
Tungsten	$_{74}W^{185}$	78.5 d	0.430	none
Rhenium	$_{75}Re^{186}$	88.9 h	0.934, 1.072	0.137
Iridium	$_{77}Ir^{192}$	74.4 d	0.67	0.296, 0.309, 0.3165, 0.468, 0.588, 0.605, 0.613
Gold	$_{79}Au^{198}$	2.70 d	0.290	0.412
	$_{79}Au^{199}$	3.14 d	0.251, 0.302, 0.460	0.050, 0.158, 0.208
Mercury	$_{80}Hg^{203}$	46.9 d	0.208	0.279
Thallium	$_{81}Tl^{204}$	3.56 y	0.764	none
Polonium	$_{84}Po^{210}$	138.4 d	5.31(α)	0.804

Glossary

Accelerator: An instrument that uses electric and magnetic fields to increase the energy of an ion.

Alpha decay: A mode of radioactive decay in which the mass number of the atom is decreased by 4 and the atomic number is decreased by 2.

Angstrom: The unit of length corresponding to atomic diameters; 1 angstrom (1A) = 10^{-8} cm.

Atomic number: The number of protons in the nucleus of an atom or ion.

Auger electrons: Low-energy electrons that are emitted from atoms when electrons fall from high to lower energy levels as a result of the photoelectric or Compton effects or electron-capture decay.

Barrier tunneling: The penetration of an energy barrier by a particle whose energy is lower than the height of the barrier.

Beta decay: A mode of radioactive decay in which the mass number remains unchanged but the atomic number is increased (negatron decay) or decreased (positron decay) by 1.

Binding energy: The amount of energy necessary to decompose a nucleus into its component nucleons.

Bremsstrahlung: Low-energy X rays emitted when electrons are decelerated and bent in their paths by the coulomb fields of atomic nuclei.

Compound nucleus: The excited nucleus that exists in the course of a nuclear reaction for approximately 10^{-14} sec after amalgamation of a bombarding particle with the target nucleus.

Compton effect: The direct interaction of a gamma ray with an orbital electron, resulting in ionization of the electron and a decrease in energy of the gamma ray.

144

Coulomb barrier: The potential-energy barrier that repulses the approach of positively charged particles to nuclei.

Critical mass: The minimum amount of a fissionable material such as U^{235} that can sustain a chain fission reaction.

Cross section: The probability of occurrence of a nuclear reaction, expressed in square centimeters; 1 barn $= 10^{-24}$ cm^2.

Decay scheme: A method of representing the modes of decay of a radioactive nucleus, the relative abundances of these decay modes, and the energies and sequence of emission of the radiations.

Electron capture: A mode of radioactive decay in which the nucleus absorbs an orbital electron, usually from the K or L shell. In this process, the mass number remains unchanged but the atomic number is decreased by 1.

Electron volt: The amount of energy acquired by a unit electronic charge when it is accelerated through a potential difference of 1 volt; $1 \text{ keV} = 10^3 \text{ eV}; 1 \text{ MeV} = 10^6 \text{ eV}$.

Energy levels: The energy states in which nuclei can exist, even if for only very short intervals of time in most cases. The lowest energy level is termed the ground state.

Fallout: The radioactive debris from atomic explosions that settles back to earth.

Fermi: The unit of length corresponding to the diameters of nuclei; 1 fermi (1 f) $= 10^{-12}$ cm $= 10^{-4}$ A.

Fission: The mode of nuclear disintegration in which the nucleus is broken into two fragments of equal or nearly equal mass with the liberation of approximately 200 MeV of energy.

Gamma decay: A mode of nuclear de-excitation in which neither the mass number nor the atomic number is changed.

Half-life: The period of time in which 50 per cent of the original number of radioactive atoms decay.

Half-thickness: The thickness of material necessary to reduce the incident-radiation intensity by 50 per cent.

Ionization potential: The amount of energy required to remove an electron from an atom, ion, or molecule.

Ion pair: The electron and the positive ion formed by the interaction of radiation with an atom or a molecule.

Isobars: Nuclides that possess the same mass numbers; e.g., Ar^{40}, K^{40}, and Ca^{40} are isobars.

Isomers: Different energy states of the same nucleus; e.g., Br^{80m} is an isomeric state having 86 KeV more energy than the ground state

Br^{80g}. Br^{80m} decays with a half-life of 4.4 hours to Br^{80g} whereas the latter decays with a half-life of 18 min to Kr^{80}.

Isotones: Nuclides that possess the same neutron numbers; e.g., $_6C^{12}$ and $_7N^{13}$ are isotones.

Isotopes: Nuclides that possess the same atomic numbers; e.g., $_{11}Na^{22}$, $_{11}Na^{23}$, and $_{11}Na^{24}$ are isotopes of sodium.

Luminescence: The emission of light as a result of the decay of an excited molecule to a lower energy level. In fluorescence, the emission of light immediately ceases upon removal of the source of excitation. In phosphorescence, the emission continues for a measurable period after removal of the excitation source.

Magic numbers: The numbers of protons or neutrons in nuclei that appear to be associated with the complete filling of energy-level shells.

Mesons: Subatomic particles having very short lifetimes outside the nucleus. The different kinds of mesons range in mass from about 200 times to almost 3000 times the weight of an electron; they may be negatively or positively charged or neutral.

Negatron: An electron of unit negative charge.

Nuclear model: A theory concerning the nature of the nucleus that is useful in explaining a set of experimental facts. The three principal nuclear models are:

1. The liquid-drop model: nucleus is treated as an oscillating, incompressible drop of liquid.

2. The shell model: nucleons in the nucleus exist in definite, individual energy levels.

3. The collective model: nucleus has a liquid-drop core of nucleons and an almost independent shell structure for the nucleons outside the core.

Nuclear spin: The intrinsic angular momentum of a nucleus in a certain energy state. Spin is expressed in multiples of $h/2\pi$ units of angular momentum, where h is Planck's constant (6.624×10^{-2} erg-sec).

Nucleon: General term for neutrons and protons in a nucleus; e.g., $_6C^{12}$ has 12 nucleons in the nucleus.

Nuclide: General term for any nuclear species; e.g., $_6C^{12}$, $_6C^{14}$, $_{20}Ca^{40}$, $_{63}Eu^{151}$, and $_{90}Th^{232}$ are all nuclides.

Pair production: The interaction of a gamma ray with the coulomb field of a nucleus to form an electron and a positron.

Photoelectric effect: The interaction of a gamma ray with an atom or a molecule, resulting in complete absorption of the gamma ray and ionization of an electron.

Plasma: An extremely hot gas that consists of ions and electrons.

Positron: An electron of unit positive charge.

Reactor: A device for sustaining a fission chain reaction at a controlled level.

Thermal neutron: A neutron whose energy corresponds to that of a gas molecule at the same temperature—approximately 0.02 eV at room temperature.

Thermonuclear reaction: The fusion of nuclei of approximately similar masses (e.g., H^3 and H^2), resulting in the release of a relatively large amount of energy.

Threshold energy: The minimum energy thermodynamically necessary for a reaction to occur.

Index